It'll Be Fine

a true story

Rebecca Rose

Rebecca Rose Press

Rebecca Rose Press

Helping Others Press On

rebecca@rebeccarosepress.com

www.rebeccarosepress.com

This book is a narrative nonfiction. The author has tried to recreate events and conversations from her memories of them. All names, some locations, and a few identifying details have been changed to protect the privacy of individuals and the security of confidential matters. In recreating this story, the author needed to adapt certain parts of the book to avoid interrupting the momentum of the narrative. Nevertheless, the story remains true overall.

Rebecca Rose Press First Edition 2016
Editing by Jillian Deganhart and Monica James
Cover Design by Jenny Heguy, JBK Website Designs
Photographs by Ashleigh Klausner, RAW Reflections
Book Layout Copyright ©2013 BookDesignTemplates.com

ISBN-10: 0-9983177-0-5
ISBN-13: 978-0-9983177-0-0

Dedication:

For all those trapped beneath the bell jar.

This is for you.

"If you want to know love, you must allow the armor of fear to be stripped from you, piece by piece, until you are naked before the world."

~Teal Swan

Chapter 1

I don't know why I said yes even though I didn't want to. Perhaps it was his mild persistence, what he would later describe in military lingo as "working a contact." Or, more likely, it was a subconscious move born out of years of romantic frustration. I was not attracted to him. Never had been. Not even remotely over all of the years I knew him. Forever ingrained in my memory was the obnoxious boy my kid brother, Benny, used to pal around with. The one who made too many *Star Wars* references, played too much Halo, and drank way too much alcohol at an inappropriately early age.

This is how it happened.

The better part of a decade had passed since I'd last seen him, when he randomly started sending me private messages on Facebook. The first I received was innocent enough. He said, "Hi, Mila. I haven't talked to you in ages. How the hell are you? What are you up to these days? Keeping Ben in line, I hope?"

At this stage in my life, I was used to men sending me messages, trying to open the door for something more than just friendly conversation. I couldn't blame them. I mean, how else are you supposed to meet somebody in the hustle and bustle of the twenty-first century? Online meet-and-greet apps were already the norm for busy single adults eager to meet someone. Through my own exposure to online dating services, I'd learned that oftentimes it was easier not to respond at all if you weren't interested, rather than responding politely and inadvertently encouraging further communication.

Before deciding whether I wanted to write him back, I attempted to view his profile to glean any information I could from it. I was unsure if I'd be able to see it since I presumed we weren't friends on Facebook. He never showed up in my newsfeed.

To my surprise, we actually were friends. I never noticed him in my newsfeed because his profile was basically inactive. Apparently he never posted, shared, or liked anything.

I scrolled through his profile pictures, all three of them. His first picture was an ancient photo probably taken around the time he graduated high school, I supposed around the same time he set up his account. The picture was blurry and he looked rather unattractive. A sloppy smile, glossy eyes, and overly relaxed stance evidenced his intoxication. *Go figure.* The second picture was an action shot of him taking a huge bite out of a hamburger. Yet again, rather unattractive. His third and final profile picture, last updated five years earlier, was an underwater shot of him in scuba gear. The scuba gear combined with the poor quality of the underwater photo made it barely possible to even recognize him.

I imagined he hadn't updated his photo in the last five years because he had presumably grown fat from drinking too much or had some other unpleasant reason to hide his current appearance. Generally speaking, people who are on Facebook but do not post pictures, status updates, or demonstrate any other kind of activity, fall into the undesirable category of "creeper status." Red flag number one.

I noticed a few girls with limited English-speaking skills and questionable grammar had commented on his timeline. For example, Angelica posted, "ive been long time w/o talkin to u ... how r u bb? where u go?" I clicked on her name and easily determined she was from Colombia. There were other similar posts from young South American women, none of which he responded to. I wasn't sure exactly what to make of it but knew one thing for certain: it was weird. Red flag number two.

His profile indicated a high school education only, did not list a career, and revealed he lived in a small town near New Orleans, Louisiana. For all I could tell, he was some bum living near the most eccentric party city in the nation, a city famous for bars that never close and streets that smell of piss, vomit, and stale liquor. I could, without difficulty, envision a kid like him growing up into a miserable man whose main goal in life was to situate himself in such a way that would allow easy access to Bourbon Street debauchery such as "boobs for beads." I could easily imagine him being precisely the kind of guy who would all too joyfully toss a tipsy girl a plastic beaded necklace as some kind of reward for showing her tits to strangers in public. Classy stuff. Red flag number three.

As the old adage goes, three strikes and you're out. Message deleted.

About a month later he pinged me again. "Hi, Mila. I'm not sure if you got my message last month. Sorry if contacting you out of the blue seemed strange. I saw the incredible pictures your sister-in-law took of you on my newsfeed, and like every other guy on the face of the planet, wanted to say hi. ☺ You should be a model, and your sister-in-law should be a professional photographer!"

I debated again whether or not I should respond to his message. I felt a little bad for making so many assumptions based on a profile he plainly put little effort in maintaining. And even if he were a loser, there was no need for me to flat-out ignore him, especially since he was my brother's childhood friend and was paying me a compliment.

I caved and replied, "Thank you for the compliment. My sister-in-law has a passion for photography. It's fun being her guinea pig. She is unbelievably talented. Sorry I didn't respond to your first message. My job keeps me busy. Must have forgotten with my hectic schedule."

It was only a partial lie. My job did keep me busier than I wanted. My life was hectic. Besides, I needed a response that would effectually tee me up for a good excuse to avoid further conversation.

Several weeks later he finally responded to me. "I know the feeling. My job keeps me busy as well. What do you do nowadays?"

I guess the fact that it took him several weeks to respond piqued my curiosity. I thought he was going to respond immediately, being a fat, drunk, desperate loser with no life and all. I had already prepared a reply that would shut down further dialogue. But since he was tolerably annoying and evidently employed, a couple of weeks later in a brief moment of boredom I replied to his message. I told him I was a CPA for a public accounting firm in Denver. I purposely didn't ask the common courtesy follow-up question "What do you do?" in the hope that my subtle hint would dissuade further messaging.

At first, I thought my hint had worked. I didn't hear a peep from him for about a month. Then he eventually wrote back. "A CPA, huh? That sounds awful! On the plus side, I'm sure you make great money. ☺ I'm currently stationed down in the swamps of Louisiana. My SWCC team is getting ready to deploy to Honduras for the next six months or so. Would you mind giving me your e-mail address? I'd like to e-mail you while I'm down there. It's not a good idea to access Facebook on these types of deployments."

I decided not to reply to his message. I didn't want him getting the wrong idea. I had a boyfriend at the time—albeit, nothing serious—but, more importantly, I wasn't interested in him. Since he wouldn't have access to Facebook for the next six months, it was the perfect opportunity to shake him.

His message did help me understand, though, why his profile seemed inactive and why young foreign women left pitiful messages on his timeline asking "where u go?" Typical single military guy: unattached and footloose. Women come and go easily for these fellas, the wiser the women the sooner. *Poor naive girls*, I mused.

About six months later when he returned from Honduras, I received yet another message from him. *Oh good God, here we go again,* I thought impatiently. Once more, I replied a few weeks later with a dry, uninviting response, hoping I would not have to spell out my disinterest.

This pattern persisted for the next year. Yes, a whole year. Why, one might ask, did I not just ignore him or tell him to bug off or, for that matter, simply block him on Facebook? I don't know why. Maybe because he was Ben's friend, and I love Ben. Or, I suppose, the messages were sporadic enough I didn't find him entirely bothersome. There might also be a teeny-tiny chance I actually enjoyed the attention a little bit, too.

While I did deliberately avoid responding to some of his messages, he would steadily but not overwhelmingly write me a little something, nothing too forward or personal, just enough to keep his toe in the door. When he finally got around to asking me out, almost two years after he first reached out to me, all the stars in heaven aligned in his favor. Just a month before, heck, even just a day before, I would've declined, but something this time changed my mind.

He caught me in a bizarre mood one evening subsequent to breaking up with my boyfriend (a different boyfriend: a more serious one, but a long-distance one). Incoherent on the hazardous concoction of loneliness and spite, I found myself carelessly accepting his invitation to dinner. After a solid night's rest, I realized my error and began mentally recalling my favorite cache of cancellation excuses.

As tempting as it was to backtrack, I ultimately decided to punish myself for my moment of weakness. How else would I learn to stop making stupid choices if I didn't have to pay the penalty? *It's one harmless date,* I internally rationalized. *I'll just go and tell him face-to-face I'm not interested since apparently I'm gonna have to stop beatin' around the bush and talk turkey to him anyway. Maybe then he'll finally get it.*

Chapter 2

Wesley Blackwell was home on leave for a few weeks around Christmas time. I knew very little about his military experience. In one of his initial messages to me, he mentioned he was part of a SWCC team stationed down in the swamps of Louisiana. I had no idea what SWCC meant and at the time didn't care enough to ask for details.

If I had to guess, though, I would think it had something to do with computer science since most of my memories of him involved the military sci-fi video game, Halo. He and my brother's posse played that game relentlessly and, if I do say so myself, quite pathetically. Wes would sneak a case of beer down to my brother's room in my parents' basement, and they would commence their eight-hour Halo marathon. Those boys were classic video and computer game nerds.

Furthermore, I doubted Wes possessed the physical requirements necessary for a combat-type position in the military. In high school he was skinny and definitely not athletic. His only tie to sports was as a spectator, a drunk and insufferable one.

Not wanting to look totally clueless on our date, I did a quick Google search. I learned SWCC stands for special warfare combatant-craft crewmen, which is a special naval operations force that controls an inventory of small craft used to support special-ops missions. SWCC are trained extensively in covert infiltration and exfiltration. Advanced weaponry tactics along with the ability to simultaneously provide rapid mobility in shallow, perilous waters represented only a couple of the skill requirements I found listed online. In short, the selection process for this kind of operator mandates physical fitness and strategic intelligence that is combat focused.

What the fuck? Did I get my wires crossed somehow? There's no way skinny, spazzy Wes made it through selections for this kind of work. No fuckin' way. I must've misunderstood him.

Reading about SWCC fascinated me, though. It was a real man's job. The work of a warrior. The natural inquisitor in me wanted to know more, so I continued to surf the web. In doing so, I discovered I was pronouncing SWCC wrong. As cumbersome as it was, I was pronouncing each individual letter in the acronym. I found out it's actually pronounced "swick," which I recognized as a word I'd heard before somewhere but used in a different context. Another Google search led me to an entry in the Urban Dictionary. Come to find out, swick is a slang word used by today's youth to describe something awesome. It's the brilliant marriage of the derivative words "sweet" and "sick." *Hmmm ... pretty apropos.*

Before I could stop myself, I was headlong in a daydream, not about Wes, but one of those James Bond characters who carries a concealed weapon everywhere he goes. I liked the thought of a man constantly carrying a weapon and expertly employing it. I grew up around guns. My dad, a lifelong farmer and avid hunter, is a serious aficionado, owning enough guns to warrant his own hunting shack—a single-wide trailer filled with six large gun cases, two reloading stations, several wall mounts, and enough hunting gear to outfit an entire army. With my dad's encouragement, I completed the hunter safety course in my early teens and have personally owned guns ever since.

Be that as it may, as my daydream progressed, I unintentionally started considering the unpleasant details associated with one of the military's "quiet professionals." Hunting animals is one thing; hunting people is quite another. I doubted how much anyone could trust an individual who had gained the kind of clearance that prevented him from discussing the majority of what he did. These kinds of professionals are qualified to exterminate national enemies, handle dangerous prisoners of war, collect and conceal confidential information, and God knows what else. It disturbed me to think of what this kind of individual might be capable of, what he might have seen and done, and what he had conceivably grown calloused to.

Also, I pictured a SWCC guy as an adrenaline junky, one of those men who successfully dodged death a time or two and consequently became addicted to its livening allure. Wouldn't he have to be, to take on a position that meant he'd be the target of bullets, bombs, torpedoes, missiles, and whatever else it is that we humans are currently using to kill each other? To volunteer for an occupation that required tactical mobility in dangerous enemy waters? That called for free falls and static line jumps? Fast roping and rappelling out of military aircraft? That demanded expert marksmanship with advanced weaponry in lethal situations?

I suspected a person exposed to this level of action would never find a boring CPA, like me, engaging for long. And that's precisely where my daydream ended.

I dolled myself up in a tight top, short skirt, and tall leather boots. I curled my long, silky, strawberry–caramel hair and applied lip-gloss that shimmered and smelled like vanilla frosting. Because I loved how it emphasized my long lashes and gray-blue eyes, I brushed on a few extra layers of midnight black mascara. When I was in college, a MAC makeup artist taught me how to apply blush and bronzer to best accentuate my facial features. She happened to be giving free makeovers at the mall that day.

"You have a beautifully heart-shaped face," she said sweetly.

I thanked her for the compliment, and she continued to demonstrate how to use the various products at her counter. "You definitely don't require a lot of makeup because your cheekbones and jawline are already very prominent, and you have a nice healthy, rosy complexion to begin with."

She removed my makeup and started applying fresh layers of powder. "With a light bronzer, just follow beneath your cheekbones to accentuate a shadow effect. Add a little beneath your jawline, too. Then dab a little bit of highlighter directly on your cheekbones and jaw muscles like this," she explained as she softly powdered, blended, and contoured my face.

When she was done, she stood back and admired her artistry. "You should really be a model with a face like that, you know?" I realized she was merely trying to flatter me so I'd buy makeup from her counter. Nevertheless, the memory stayed with me, and I've applied my makeup that way ever since.

I finished beautifying myself and put on my golden-brown leather jacket that seamlessly matched my leather boots. I took one final look in the mirror and smiled at my reflection, preened and primped to a state of nearly impossible perfection. Feeling quite irresistible, I answered the door with a sparkling smile, only to be dumbfounded by a smile even brighter and more buoyant than my own. The man at my door possessed the kind of smile that occupied every part of his face—his eyes, his cheeks, there was even a shallow dimple.

My breath caught in my throat, and my mind suddenly went blank. I tried unsuccessfully to think of something to say as I struggled to wipe the look of shock off my face. Instead of seeing my brother's skinny, dorky high school friend, or an obese, inebriated grown-up version of him, I was confronted by a poised, muscular, dream of a man with dark curly hair, designer facial scruff, perfect almond complexion and turbulent eyes, lusty with life. And that smile.

"Wesley?" I finally managed to croak after an awkward silence, still squinting my eyes in disbelief.

He laughed. His laugh reminded me of the low, comforting notes on the church piano my mother played every weekend. "Yep, that's me." He gracefully pulled me toward him to greet me with a hug. The intoxicating scent of his Calvin Klein cologne cast a lingering cloak of fragrance about me that I enjoyed long after the hug ended. He grabbed my shoulders and gently pushed me back at arm's length. He took me in with his eyes. "Well don't you look pretty," he acclaimed as he gave me the once-over, his gaze sweeping rapidly over me.

I should've riposted, "Not nearly as pretty as you." But still trying to gather my wits, I meekly muttered, "Thank you," and followed him as he led me to the passenger side door of his car.

I couldn't help but notice his distinctive walk as I followed him. He walked with what I now like to call a military swagger—chest out, shoulders back, and head high, with an assertive yet easygoing stride. Some might describe his walk as cavalier or cocky, but the only adjective that crossed my mind was sexy.

I was so distracted by the sight of him in those first moments as we walked toward the car that I completely forgot how cold it was outside. Colorado winter is no time to be wearing a short summer skirt. I knew that much. But I also knew my long legs looked good in it. My philosophy, foolishly, was fashion before function.

He decided to take me to a nearby steakhouse. Other than asking me a couple of brief questions confirming directions to the restaurant, the short car ride remained relatively silent. I was grateful for the silence because my mind was still trying to play catch-up with my eyes. I instinctively started developing a new set of expectations of the stranger sitting next to me. I remembered the information I read online about his job. At the time, I was certain I misunderstood him. I couldn't reconcile the Wes I knew as an adolescent with that job description. However, seeing him now and the partially concealed Glock 19 on his hip, I knew that at least some of my former assumptions, if not all, were dead wrong.

As he quietly steered the vehicle through congested traffic, his momentary taciturnity made me wonder if he was like many other military men, hard and not given to much emotional expression. I knew that oftentimes combat had an eerie way of creeping into a soldier's psyche. How could it not? Some of the things they saw and did were bound to have an effect on their spirit. I'd heard rumors in my hometown community that his older brother suffered from post-traumatic stress disorder from his time deployed in Iraq. Did that make Wesley especially susceptible to a similar reaction?

I flicked a sideways glance at him, attempting to see through his impassive exterior. The short stubble on his face gave him an intriguingly dangerous look. He caught me gaping and instantly that captivating smile of his transformed his entire face. I felt myself relax a little. I had to remind myself that this was just a friendly, casual date headed nowhere. It didn't matter what issues he might have. It also didn't matter if I found him handsome and mysteriously beguiling. Nothing could change the fact that we lived completely opposite lives in completely different states.

Dinner opened with a house appetizer, fresh hot rolls with a sweet cinnamon butter. I ordered a savory prime rib, loaded baked potato, and green beans marinated in an onion and bacon brine. It was definitely my kind of restaurant. Wes confessed, rather charmingly, that he texted my brother before our date to determine the best place to take me. I liked that he did his research, and I was beginning to learn that I could expect nothing less from a guy like him.

He ordered something healthy with salmon and veggies. "Who orders salmon at a steakhouse?" I teased him. He laughed and agreed it was a poor choice. "Lucky for you, I only ate half my meal. Have at it." I attempted to trade plates with him.

"No, you need to eat it, Mila. You're too fuckin' skinny," he bluntly criticized as he pushed the plate back in my direction.

I rolled my eyes as I snapped back, "I'll take that as a compliment."

"Don't," he recoiled, shaking his head.

"I'm just gonna feed it to my dog if you don't eat it," I blithely threatened as I raised my hand and pretended to waive down the waiter for a to-go box.

"Fine," he conceded, exhaling his frustration. I dropped my hand with a wicked little smirk of victory on my face and handed him the plate. "I'll eat it this time. But seriously," he pointed a finger at me like a perturbed parent, "you could stand to eat more."

"I don't have a big appetite," I countered. "I love food, but I don't require a ton of it ... evidently like some people." I judgmentally looked at him as he shoveled mounds of food in his mouth.

Wes gazed at me suspiciously as he finished chewing a ginormous bite of prime rib. "Do you exercise?"

I paused temporarily, drawn back to a different phase of my life, before I answered. "Truthfully, no." I speedily added, "I used to be very athletic, though." I started to say something more when he interjected.

"I know. I remember you from high school. Ben used to get so mad at me for ogling you at your volleyball games. I mean those spandex. C'mon. They were practically underwear. They made your ass look phenomenal!" He flashed a devilish smile at me, working his flirtation engines hard.

My eyes widened a bit. "Hey, I didn't pick out the uniforms. Besides, I'd never hike my shorts up as high as most of the girls." I lifted my chin and looked down my nose at him before I innocently shrugged my shoulders and proceeded to explain. "I think I burned myself out by the time I hit college. I played sports year-round practically my whole life—always training for something. I was worn out. So, I decided to dedicate all that extra energy to a worthy cause: academics. Graduating summa cum laude from the honors program at Regis is no modest undertaking, mind you."

A giant guilty grin involuntarily made its way across my face. Actually, maintaining a perfect GPA at Regis University didn't seriously present a challenge to me, even though it is one of Colorado's most acclaimed private universities. Yet that's not to say I didn't put forth a lot of effort. My need for perfection drove me to study habitually, definitely more than 90 percent of the student base. I easily could've gotten by with much less while still receiving an A+ for the course, but I didn't solely want an A+, I wanted to be the *best*.

Academic pursuits meant more to me than most, I suppose. Academics were fair. They gave you what you deserved. They could be calculated, mastered, understood, and relied on, unlike people and relationships. I earned a lifetime track record of perfect transcripts, never receiving a final grade below an A. I graduated high school as class valedictorian, yet that didn't mean much to me since there were seven other students that tied for the same honor when really only one student, besides myself, merited the accolade.

The high school I attended was small and behind the times. It didn't offer advanced placement courses that weighted a student's GPA. This bothered me because I was applying for the Boettcher Scholarship, one of the most esteemed full-ride scholarships offered solely in the state of Colorado. The application process was extensive and incredibly competitive, and I had been planning to apply ever since one of my junior high teachers told me I had "a real shot at it." I worried a 4.0 GPA looked insufficient compared to the thousands of other applicants who carried a GPA above mine. I planned my entire high school agenda with the Boettcher Scholarship centered in my sights.

I held a leadership position in practically every extracurricular activity under the sun. The most competitive leadership position was student council president. Traditionally this spot was awarded to a senior. Underclassmen, although eligible for the position, didn't dare run for it. Seniors were supposed to win every year. It was an unspoken matter of fact.

On a whim I dared to run against the seniors my junior year and astonishingly won the student body vote. The second runner-up hated me for it—she thought I had stolen some kind of birthright from her—but I didn't care. It might seem calloused to admit, but other people's feelings couldn't get in the way of my success.

I tried not to act that way, though. Calloused, that is. In fact, outwardly, I was exceptionally sweet and gracious, which is probably how I won the student body vote two years in a row. Teachers and students alike described me as a delight or as a thoughtful, caring person. I volunteered much of my time and was friends with everyone, even the unpopular kids. But deep down it was all about numero uno. Unlike many of my peers, there was no college fund patiently waiting for me on graduation day. High school was a cutthroat business, and I knew precisely what needed to be done, academically and socially, in order to stack the scholarship odds in my favor.

Between my classes, tutoring other students, all of my extracurricular activities, and year-round sports, I spent more hours at the high school than the majority of the teaching and administrative staff. At the time, nothing meant more to me than winning the Boettcher. I did everything in my power to make my dream a reality. I even made silly promises to God that I'd routinely go to daily mass while procuring my undergraduate degree if He'd just answer my one prayer and deliver the Boettcher to me.

My hard work and dedication paid off beautifully the day I was awarded the scholarship. My big prayer was answered, unlike in future years.

"Frankly, it's been over five years since I've purposely exercised," I apathetically spilled the beans. I easily read the expression of disapproval on his face, but was sort of proud of the fact I had managed to stay so thin without deliberating trying. I chalked it up to good genes, especially since I succeeded in not only not exercising but also drinking an average of three Mountain Dews and eating at least one, but most likely two, fast-food meals per day. By all accounts, I should've weighed about 300 pounds, not 120.

"So does this conclude the story of how you lost your ass?" he rhetorically asked. "I'm not very impressed, Mila. I know you're bullshittin' me. I'm thinkin', yeah okay, it's probably true that you were burned out on sports, but I know you weren't spending *all* your time with your nose in the books." He shook his head and grinned. "We're gonna need to work on that. Your ass is as flat as a pancake. I can't even tell where your back ends and your legs begin. It's just weird."

I sat there for a moment trying to filter what I really wanted to say. *You cocky son of a bitch. How dare you insult my body? You think you're all high 'n' mighty now because you don't look like some skinny fuckin' freak anymore? Well, guess what? I give zero shits about what you think of my ass.*

I closed my eyes, took a deep breath, nodded with as much grace as I could muster, and cursed him beneath my genial smile. "Yeah, well, I guess I'd rather not have an ass than be an ass." I regarded him accusingly. "You're lucky I'm a confident woman, Wesley, otherwise, I might be liable to use this steak knife here." I picked up the knife and jokingly made stabbing motions in his direction.

He grabbed his right hip, the one harboring the Glock 19. "Never bring a knife to a gunfight, my dear." We both laughed at the morbidity of our buffoonery. I laid down my knife and put my hands in the air to signify my surrender. He reached across the table and grabbed my hands, holding them in his own as the conversation continued to flow. The sweetness of the gesture helped me forgive his rude comment, however true it might've been.

And it was true, which is why it hit a sensitive chord—well, that and the fact I was stubbornly trying to lie to myself about not being ashamed of how I let my healthy, athletic body go. His comment brought to surface feelings of guilt and self-disgust I had semi-successfully buried along with a lot of other emotions. Even if heroine-addict-thin was the fad in high fashion, it wasn't healthy, and I knew it. There was nothing healthy about me anymore, except maybe my bank account and long list of achievements.

While we clearly didn't agree on everything, conversation flowed effortlessly throughout dinner. The topics were lighthearted in nature, and we both laughed and teased a lot.

His whole torso tightened when he laughed. The earth-toned flannel shirt he wore had the top two buttons undone, and my eyes kept falling to his brawny chest. *This must be how guys feel when a woman is showing cleavage*, I supposed, while attempting to keep my gaze from noticeably dropping.

I didn't want dinner to end. I couldn't remember the last time I appreciated conversing with someone so much. He wasn't just easy on the eyes; he was easy to talk to. There was something refreshing about his personality.

He seemed to be one of those rare people who felt completely comfortable in his own skin. He wasn't preoccupied with pretending to be something he wasn't. There was no filter on his mouth, and I'm not merely referring to his ability to employ curse words with virtuosic skill. He wasn't apologetic about thinking differently than the social memes of our culture. He didn't allow his thoughts and actions to be driven by other people's notions of what he should do or be. His independence of mind, though a little unpolished and sometimes impetuous, was generally pretty spot-on and quenching to my ears, which had been parched in the pretentious political correctness and fakeness of the professional world.

I couldn't say the same about myself, obviously. I had installed a perma-filter in my voice box years ago. It had started small and gradually mutated into a hideous routine of placating others for the sake of what I thought was personal gain.

Over the course of time, I steadily lost my identity and became one of those smarmy sycophants who are all too eager to sacrifice a tiny piece of their soul in order to win some scrap of approval, acknowledgement, or achievement. I understood the importance of benevolence as a means to more self-serving objectives. I learned that manipulating people's perceptions of me by always being a likeable, affable version of myself was one of the surest ways to fuel my success in ego-driven goals.

At one point in my life, long before I became the Brainiac, I used to be more like Wes. In his deportment, I saw a reflection of the girl I once was. He made me nostalgic for her.

Chapter 3

During the drive back to my house, Wesley nonchalantly asked me what I thought about long-distance relationships. Without skipping a beat, the jaded part of me reacted. "I don't think about them. They're not even worth considering. They never work out." Almost as soon as I finished saying it, the bottom of my stomach gave way. I didn't want to admit it, but I liked him. I liked him a lot more than I was expecting to, way more than I was supposed to.

There was something about him that just pulled me in. I obviously barely knew him, but somehow passing on the potential opportunity of spending more time with him still stung.

His occupational choice plainly meant a lot of time away from home which predictably brings its own slew of issues, particularly in a romantic relationship. I was still smarting from long-distance woes with a man I had truly loved. A man I had carried a torch for since the first grade. A man I prayed I'd be lucky enough to spend the rest of my life with. I had no interest in repeating such anguish. I admittedly went so far that I swore I'd never do that again.

I stole a quick glimpse of Wes, trying to read how my response made him feel, but he was expressionless. His face gave away nothing.

We pulled into the driveway. He put the car in park, briskly said goodnight, and waited for me to get out. I said goodnight in the same brisk fashion and exited the vehicle just in time for a gust of wind to catch me off guard. The icy breeze nipped at my bare thighs and swirled my hair around my face. The arctic jolt threw me off balance, and before I could stop it, I was slipping on the ice. I fell, hitting the frozen concrete as if I wore a lead collar around my neck. Wes leaped out of the car and ran over to me just as I was pulling myself upright.

"Are you okay?" he asked right away. A look of concern softened his features.

"Yes," I half-laughed, knowing how idiotic I must look. He grabbed my freezing hands and helped me to my feet. Recognizing I wasn't seriously injured, an air of amusement swiftly spread across his face. He coquettishly offered to help wipe the snow off the bare skin of my thighs. Before I could say anything, he started delicately brushing my naked skin, and as if by magic, a hot sensation cut through the cold.

Even though I was slightly irritated by the humiliating, frosty assault and his obvious enjoyment at my displeasure, the feeling of his warm hands on my thighs made me suddenly blurt out, "Do you wanna come in?" I think the invitation surprised me more than it surprised him.

I rarely invited men into my house, and certainly never on a first date. I was anything but promiscuous. For being just shy of twenty-six years old, I had slept with an exceptionally small number of men. I presumed that could be attributed to my strict Catholic upbringing, yet I hadn't considered myself Catholic in over five years. I liked to think my sexual prudence reflected a high grade of self-respect; however, I knew it derived from much more than just that.

In the widely philandering culture of the twenty-first century, many of my peers would've thought it peculiar that I'd had so few sexual partners by the time I'd reached my mid-twenties. And to some degree, they would've been right. The story of my sexual journey was ill-fated.

"Sure," Wes replied with a smile. "Lemme kill the engine." He closed my car door, ran to the driver's side, pulled the keys from the ignition, and followed me to the front door while grabbing my hips to provide support. His hands on my hips triggered a warm liquid feeling in my belly.

Upon entering the house, I told him I wanted to take my boots off and change my clothes and that he should make himself comfortable. Like a gentleman, he slipped his shoes off at the door to avoid getting the light-colored carpet dirty. When I came out of my bedroom with sweatpants and a hoodie on, I found him knelt over the fireplace gently blowing on a small flame. *Well isn't he perfect*, I hopelessly thought to myself.

"Thank you. That was thoughtful of you." I walked toward the fire.

"You looked pretty cold." He winked at me.

"You're welcome," I grinned, remembering the feeling of his warm hands on my freezing thighs.

He snickered and said, "Yes, thank *you*." As he laughed, the light of the flames flickered across his strong upper body, and suddenly I felt a little flushed. I moved away from the fire and snuggled up to a velvety red pillow on my black leather couch. I sat lengthwise on the couch so I could get my feet up off the cold hardwood floor.

After the fire was blazing, Wes sat down next to me, gently grabbed my legs, and pulled them over his lap as he scooted close. "There," he said almost in a whisper. Butterflies fluttered in my chest cavity. His tender yet assertive manner cast some kind of spell over me. *What would it be like to kiss him?* I found myself wondering, but almost immediately pushed the thought away.

"This is a nice place," he observed. "I'm kinda surprised you live in this big house all by yourself. I noticed the 'For Sale' sign when I pulled up."

"Yeah, I put it on the market about a month ago. It's honestly a little too much for me to handle all by myself, especially considering how many hours I spend at the office every week. Though I do love having a big yard for my dog, Benelli, and my cat, Ruger." One of Wesley's hands shot up as he interrupted me.

"Hold on a sec, you named your pets after gun makers?" He nodded his head in approval. "I have a feeling we're gonna be good friends, Mila." He squeezed one of my legs.

I grinned widely and continued my train of thought, "Well, Nelli and Ruger definitely seem to appreciate all the space to roam, but I just can't seem to keep up with everything the way I want to, so I put the house up for sale." I chose not to disclose how I felt afraid in the house all by myself, even with my big dog and the shotgun I kept chambered within arm's reach of my pillow.

My fear of being alone had developed about ten years earlier. In my late teens, a troubled boy a few years older than me and hooked on drugs had violated my sense of security. I grew up in a small and friendly farm town, a place where everybody knew everyone. Where the threads were woven together and recrossed between school and work and church and everything else to create a homey quilt unfamiliar to those in big cities. Quite naturally, I lived a sheltered life and believed I was safe within the boundaries of my quilted town.

Everything changed the day this neighbor boy began to repeatedly stalk and harass me. He lived only a block away and found countless opportunities to make me feel threatened, including trespassing on our property and sneaking into my bedroom in the middle of the night to steal personal items like pictures of me and underwear from my hamper. He fondled these things while masturbating, or so said the rumors.

My boyfriend at the time tracked him down one night and beat the shit out of him, but that didn't stop him. Thankfully, the situation eventually diffused before escalating into something more serious. He was arrested on multiple charges including auto theft, drug possession, and trespassing. He went to jail, and I didn't see him loitering around again for several years. Nevertheless, the situation left an ugly scar of fear on me.

My sense of security was violated again while I was studying abroad in a foreign country. A man assaulted me on a quiet side street as I walked back to my apartment from campus. I was wearing a summer dress. He snuck up behind me, forcefully grabbed my crotch through my legs from behind, and smirked like a true pervert as he molested me, then hastily ran away before

I could do anything but find the oxygen to let out a pathetic, practically inaudible scream.

I thought living alone would be a good way to challenge and hopefully rid myself of the fear that gripped me. However, I wasn't making much progress in the matter.

"What kinda dog you got?" asked Wes, thwarting my nauseating memories.

"She's a boxer-mastiff mix with beautiful brindle coloring," I answered proudly. "She's a big dog but looks more like a tiger," I giggled. "Benny playfully calls her 'Kitty.' Do you mind if I let her in? She has an insulated dog house but it's pretty cold out."

"Not at all."

I walked over to the sliding glass door that led to the backyard and pulled open the curtain. There was Nelli with her wet snout pressed up against my recently clean door. Her tail wagged so cheerfully her whole body swayed with the movement.

I was concerned about how she'd react to Wesley. Nelli was afraid of men. She was abused in her early puppyhood by her first owner, evidently a man. She had never fully trusted one since. She'd generally cower away and urinate on herself if an unfamiliar man tried to approach her.

She eventually warmed up to my brother Benny after several visits, although I could tell she was still leery of him at times. Ben is a big devil, quite literally; he towers over her at six-foot-seven, but for all of his intimidating height, he's full of nothing but mirth and goodwill. I assumed his height troubled her, but his friendly voice and jovial demeanor eventually won her over to some degree. If he made any movements that were hasty or seemingly aggressive, she hunkered down and tucked her tail between her legs while her eyes searched me out.

"She's typically fearful of men," I cautioned Wes, while I unlocked and slid open the door.

"It'll be fine," he confidently assured me.

Nelli waited for my command to cross the doorway threshold. As she waited, Ruger very smugly squeezed past her and let himself in, deliberately tickling his long fuzzy tail on her nose as he passed. My fat and furry black cat reminded me of Albert Einstein because of the large gray tufts that fanned out from his ears. He was only three years old at the time, and extremely well groomed due to the monthly baths I mandated, but those gray tufts made him look old and wise.

My darling little menace, Ruger, relished the moments when Nelli was bound by my command. He'd taunt her. If I instructed her to "stay" he'd saunter over to her and bat at her nose with his clawless paws and snappishly scamper away. Nelli would whimper and look at me with those puppy eyes that said, "Oh c'mon! Didn't you just see that?" Regardless, Nelli adored Ruger. Ruger didn't so much adore Nelli, only loved to impishly torment her.

"Okay, girl," I said as I waved Nelli across the threshold. She bounded inside, sliding on the hardwood floor. She spotted Wesley straightaway and hurried over to me, sitting directly on my feet. She stared up at me anxiously. "It's okay, girl," I soothingly whispered. I reached down to pet her velvety belly. She leaned heavily into my legs.

Wes did not try to approach us. He simply sat on the couch across the room by the fire and observed. I was relieved he didn't try to approach Nelli because she might have nervously peed on me.

I made my way back to the couch at a leisurely pace. Nelli, keeping with her routine, painfully stepped on my unprotected feet with her hard claws as she tangled herself between my legs. "Too close," I said in a low, serious tone. I skillfully kneed her powerful chest to signal to her I needed more space. She backed off about an inch.

I sat near Wes, and he sweetly lifted my legs and draped them over his lap again. "There," he smiled.

I was beginning to learn that at close range his smile was unsafe. I tried to keep my wits about me, but he made it nearly impossible. He lightly traced one of the red marks developing on the top of my foot from Nelli's claws. My heart somersaulted in my chest and did maybe some other kind of kid-like twirl.

I eyed Nelli. She rigidly parked herself next to me, but as far away from Wes as possible, watching me intently, letting out a low-pitched whine every few breaths. Wes dropped his hand near the ground and rested it there without looking at Nelli. She looked at his hand, then back up at me, then back at his hand. Back and forth her eyes shifted apprehensively. I knew she wanted a pet. Nelli deeply desired affection to the point of desperation. I waited to see how she would react. Ultimately, curiosity got the better of "Kitty."

She inched her way closer to his hand and lightly nudged it. Wes didn't react right away. She nudged it again, this time with a little enthusiasm. He mildly stroked her head and lowered his hand again. Nelli licked his hand with her disgusting, slobbery mammoth tongue. Wes shot a triumphant and toothy smile my direction.

"I can't believe she's warming up to you so quickly," I said, shaking my head incredulously.

"I can," he retaliated. "Animals tend to like me. I grew up on a ranch full of 'em, you know. Not to brag, but even half-wild animals like me."

He slipped his hand under the opening of my sweatpants near my ankle and lightly caressed my lower leg. I swallowed deeply, lubricating the dryness in my throat.

"When I was deployed in Colombia one time, an undomesticated macaw followed me around and would occasionally land on my M-4 and hitch a free ride as I hiked 'bout camp." He showed me a picture on his iPhone of a beautiful two-toned blue bird with a neon yellow breast perched on the butt of his gun in the middle of a luscious green jungle. Dressed in a brown T-shirt and camo pants, with a backpack, assault rifle, and other military gear hanging from his burly physique, an amused and victorious expression shaped Wes's tanned, younger-looking face.

Although not wholly warranted, knowing that animals, even skittish ones like Nelli, instinctively trusted Wes deepened my own sixth sense of trust in him.

"So why'd you buy this place anyway?" he prodded.

I let out a long breath before I answered. "Well, I bought it straight out of college a few years ago. I figured it'd be a solid investment, and I was fortunate enough not to have to consider school loans. The first-time homebuyer tax credit baited me into the real estate domain."

I faltered for a split second as I considered whether to share more. "Also," I dragged out the word longer than necessary. "I had a boyfriend at the time. We were starting the third year of our relationship. I assumed he'd eventually move in with me and help me maintain the place. He did end up moving in with me 'bout a year later, but he only stayed for a year. It seemed like a smart thing to do at the time. Granted, I can't fully understand how I came to that conclusion now." I sighed heavily as my mind reluctantly relived the memories shaped by the consequences of those decisions.

"Four years!" Wes looked at me wide-eyed.

It took me a second to register what he was talking about as I snapped from my flashback. "Oh. Actually, it was a total of five," I corrected him.

He snorted. "My longest 'relationship' was five *weeks*, and that's being generous." He shook his head at the comparison. The way he air quoted the word "relationship" gave the impression he didn't believe in participating in something as dull and futile as a lasting romantic bond.

"Five weeks?" I asked doubtfully. "How's that even possible? You've never had a serious girlfriend?"

"I've never wanted a girlfriend. It's not a logical choice in my profession, though some men attempt to make the impossible work."

"So ... you're more of a one-night-stand kinda guy then?" I sheepishly interrogated, not completely wanting to know the answer to my own question. "Is that what you planned for me? For tonight?" I playfully poked his tight chest but felt the beginnings of disappointment sneak into my core.

"Well yeah," he teased back as if to say "duh."

I calmly smiled and continued my interrogation. "So how many women have you been with?" I pressed. I understood it was none of my business, but I had to ask. Learning that he was a playboy alerted me to the fact that we were likely on the opposite end of the spectrum when it came to what we wanted out of a first date. I didn't want him to assume that just because I happened to invite him into my home I'd sleep with him.

"You don't wanna know," he replied. "And I won't ever tell you," he concluded with an unapologetic air that grated my nerves.

My mind raced momentarily. *Why did I invite this guy into my home? It's obvious now all he wants to do is fuck me and leave.*

Just to be clear, I didn't want a relationship with him. That much was already established. The inevitable long-distance aspect of that possibility left a piece of the puzzle missing that was infinitely important to me. Nonetheless, the immature part of me wanted *him* to want a relationship with *me*. Otherwise, my excessively analytical brain could not reconcile the reason for his long-standing determination in securing this date.

Why would he patiently persist even after I rudely blew him off so many times over the last couple of years? It couldn't be more obvious he has zero problems finding women to throw themselves at him. I just don't get it. If he doesn't want a girlfriend, if that's considered attempting the "impossible," then what's he doing here with me tonight? What kinda guy works that hard for a one-night stand?

"Is everything okay? You kinda stopped talkin'." He broke the silence of my thoughts.

"Yep, everything's fine," I lied, attempting to pretend his sexual escapades didn't affect me.

"That's a lie," he replied flatly. In hindsight, I should've known better than to try to hide my feelings from a man trained in observing and reading people. While I, too, considered myself decent at the art of analyzing others, I hadn't mastered my poker face by any means.

"Does it bother you I've slept with so many women?" He asked with an annoying simper, clearly already knowing the answer to his own question.

I didn't respond right away. A number of evasive answers popped like bubblegum on the tip of my tongue. I toyed with several clever ways to escape the question, but for some reason I answered honestly instead. "Yes." I quickly added, "Though not for the reasons you probably think." A moment of silence passed. He stared at me unwaveringly as if searching for some kind of clue in my eyes.

I reminded myself, again, it did not matter what I thought of Wesley or what he thought of me. We had no future together. I was only on this date because of a lapse in judgment in a moment of weakness.

Regardless, I didn't want our conversation to stall. It was so nice being able to talk to someone the way we talked that evening. I had rarely, if ever, talked to someone I had just met so easily and openly.

Besides, somehow the very unassuming way he'd gone about sleeping with so many women made the whole conversation seem sort of civilized. By that I mean, it seemed like he was honest with the women he slept with. From what I could tell, it wasn't as if he were some creep acting on the sly. He gave me the impression that he always explained upfront how his job prevented him from wanting to get involved. At least he was forward about it.

So I decided, even though the topic was uncomfortable for me, to keep talking. I started slowly, "It's just that ... I haven't slept with many guys. It doesn't even take me a full hand to count my number." I wiggled my five fingers in front of his unyielding eyes. "I don't know if I'm jealous of you or disgusted by you," I finished with an expression that was meant to convey my mixed emotions.

"Fuck me," he said in complete disbelief. "How the fuck did that happen, Mila? You're nearly 26 years old, incredibly beautiful, intelligent and successful." He found my hand and gave it a squeeze. "You gotta have guys flinging themselves at you everywhere you go. How do you manage to fuck less than five of them? That's insane." He tittered at the implausible thought. Then he softened his voice as he said, "It's kinda cool, though, Mila. I mean, I'd never be able to do that, nor would I want to, but it's kinda cool you did. *You* must have morals," he quipped.

"Well, I did have the same boyfriend for five years. That cut my number short for obvious reasons," I said, trying to excuse my good behavior for some reason not immediately apparent to me. And then before I could prevent it, my gaze involuntarily dropped to the floor, lost in a memory that deprived my cheeks of their color. I knew he could tell there was something I was thinking that I was reluctant to share. That there was some other truth hidden behind my confession.

Chapter 4

The truth was, my ex-boyfriend and I didn't have much sex.

Oliver was the first man I ever slept with. I was nineteen when I fell in love with him and, not too long thereafter, decided it was the right time to take our relationship to a whole new level. Subsequently, I was traumatized by the pain involved in our first attempt at intercourse. A pure manifestation of love miserably transmuted into a nightmarish disappointment. We both expected the pain to go away after a little while, but it didn't. Emotionally we were two peas in a pod, but physically we did not fit together. Lovemaking for us was about as productive as trying to thread a sausage through the eye of a needle.

We survived five years on minimal sex due to a combination of our youthful naïveté and a deeply loving friendship. In fact, the naive part of us believed we'd be lifelong partners regardless of our sex problems. I even accepted a promise ring from him the night before I departed for a semester away in Barcelona.

We tried everything to improve our intimacy issues, especially recommendations from my doctors. A few years into it, I elected to undergo a surgery aimed to remove the inflexible scar tissue (that had gradually coated my vaginal opening) with the supple skin from one of my labia. The surgery, although successful in replacing the scar tissue, did not change the size of my tiny undercarriage. The doctors eventually confirmed my greatest fear. I was born with abnormally small woman parts, and no amount of surgery was going to make my very well-endowed boyfriend fit comfortably inside me.

After five years of ruthless failures and disappointments, the whole situation became progressively unhealthy. We were forced to face the gloomy realization that years of un-enjoyable sex led to unavoidable side effects that began to rob us of the joy we once found in our affectionate relationship. In the end, out of love for one another, we made the agonizing decision to part ways. It was the hardest thing I ever had to do. Ollie was as much a part of me as my own atomic matter, bonded to my heart like a molecule. Losing him left a hole in my chest the size of a six-foot-five best friend.

After the initial shock and ache of the breakup finally receded, I became determined to experience sex with another man. I felt broken, and I needed to compare a brand-new experience to what I already knew in order to judge whether there existed a spark of hope for my future relationships. About nine months later, I wound up sleeping with some country hunk I met on vacation in South Carolina.

I spotted him right away on the beach the day I arrived. I'm pretty sure every woman within viewing distance noticed him. After a couple of hours of being coy and eyeballing each other, Brooks finally rallied the confidence to approach me. He spoke with the smoothest, sweetest Southern accent. We had few things in common and conversation content was often lacking, but I could listen to his honeyed words for hours.

He was the closest thing to a one-night stand I ever experienced. Our relationship, if you can even call it that, lasted more than one night but not by much. The sheer excitement of sleeping with a remarkably handsome man I barely knew at a romantic beach resort was so overwhelming that I was surprisingly not surprised when sex with him was painless. Sadly, I can't go so far as to describe it as climactic, but at least it didn't hurt.

Even with my encouraging experience with Brooks, negative feelings continued to cling to my outlook of sex. Growing up in a strict Catholic environment brought shame and guilt to the act. Being stalked and sexually harassed in my teens and assaulted in my early twenties added fear and anger to the mix. Enduring years of physical pain and losing Ollie stirred grief and resentment into the pot. I started to begrudge people who enjoyed sex, the way it should be. I wanted that for myself. Better yet, I needed it. I felt gypped to the point of severely souring my relationship with God and my own body.

Layer upon layer of negative feelings clung to me with the tension of a rubber band ball. Of course I didn't feel it was appropriate to throw the gory details of my sexual history at Wes, particularly on a first date. I kind of wanted to, since he possessed a unique presence that somehow shepherded a sense of calm and ease, but I worried it was all too much.

I tried to contrive a way to inconspicuously change topics. But it was too late. There was nothing inconspicuous about the pained expression held hostage on my face. The memories virtually cartwheeled out of my eyes and crashed to the cold hardwood floor. Wes's face softened in the kindest way, and then followed a comfortable moment where we just sat there looking at each other while he patiently waited for me to regain my balance.

"So ... you mentioned you're based in Louisiana," I finally managed. "Where do you live there?"

"Well," he started, "when I first moved to Louisiana, I lived in a house on the waterfront with some other swickles." I quickly interpreted "swickles" as a pet name used by SWCC guys. "A few years ago, I decided to buy a small yacht to live on. It's in Slidell for the time being."

"Wow, your life is infinitely more fascinating than mine," I whined. "You live on a yacht, travel the world, have sex with all sorts of beautiful strangers, jump out of airplanes, scuba dive, shoot all kinds of cool guns ... and I'm sittin' over here thinkin', 'Yeah, well, I can produce a killer set of financial statements, so ... prepare to have your mind blown.'" I made a masquerading movement with my hands that represented a mind exploding.

He laughed at my flamboyant sarcasm. "Maybe your job isn't interesting, Mila, but I think your personality is." He said this with the type of sincerity and stripped-of-any-kind-of-pretense kindness that is seldom found in achingly good-looking men.

"Thank you," I smiled at him and let the compliment simmer for a second. "Still, I'd rather talk about you. Tell me more about military life."

We stayed up late cuddling on the couch while chatting with ease. The ease of our banter was entirely new to me. No underlying pressure, no eggshells or minefields hidden in our conversation. I couldn't detect an agenda masked inside his words. It was real, authentic, easy, entertaining, and felt something like home.

He told me about various training schools he'd attended. His range of skills fascinated me. While I was going to school learning about debits and credits, he was going to school learning how to drive fast, pick locks, perform in high-stress situations, avoid tricky interrogation tactics, and fight with deadly force. While I was comfortably drinking my coffee and eating a bagel in class learning about spreadsheets and financial analytics, he was starving in SERE school learning how to survive, evade, resist, and escape all alone in the wintry Maine mountains.

He told me about one training exercise in the jungles of Honduras where he was supposed to play the part of a captured prisoner. He was accidentally thrown into a fire ant mound and was bitten so many times his entire body was covered with huge, itching welts. He showed me painful-looking pictures on his iPhone to prove it.

He told me about another time when he was showering on base while deployed in Iraq when suddenly the alarm sounded and shards of shrapnel came raining down around his naked body. He sprinted faster than ever to the bunker that day and afterward made jokes with nearby swickles about how he almost died in his birthday suit.

He confided in me how stupid he felt one time in Colombia when he almost lost his left hand trying to light a dissected sim grenade on fire, which is apparently an absurd experiment he attempted out of pure boredom. He and the medic, his buddy, Doc Swartz, fabricated some story about a training accident when his C.O. (commanding officer) asked why his hand was burnt to hell. Luckily, the saltwater from his diving expeditions over the next week saved his hand from scarring miserably, or at least so he presumed.

I also learned his contract with the Navy was set to expire in just a few months. Hope lurched inside me, until he followed up with the fact he'd already informed his C.O. he was planning to extend his contract by one year and complete another deployment in South America. The intention was not set in stone, it seemed, but was highly probable.

"Well it's time to get you to bed," he said, catching me in the middle of a yawn. "I'll tuck you in." He shot a mischievous sideways glance my way.

"Okay," I replied, although I didn't move. He lifted my legs off his lap and gently set them on the ground. I sleepily started walking toward my bedroom. He followed close behind while Nelli tried to weasel her way between us.

I collapsed on my bed and buried my face in the pillow. He sat down on the edge and pulled the covers over me. I turned and looked up at him, wondering if he was going to kiss me goodnight. He delicately touched my face. My heart started pounding so hard I feared he might hear it in the silence of the night. He stood up and instantly a pang of dejection cramped inside me. He gazed down at me and said goodnight.

As he turned to walk out of the room, I reached my hand out and barely touched his arm. "Wait," I said in a whisper. I hesitated, not accustomed to acting out in this kind of assertive behavior, before asking, "Will you stay until I fall asleep?"

I liked having him next to me, especially since my anxiety of intruders ran rampant in the middle of the night. I hoped with Wes next to me, I could sleep soundly for the first time in a long time. The loaded shotgun leaning in the corner closest to my reach, unfortunately, did not ease my fears as much as I would've liked.

"Sure," he agreed.

"No funny business," I pointed my finger at him like a parent warning a child.

"No funny business," he echoed, trying to look earnest through his crooked smile.

I nestled in his arms and felt perfectly comfortable, but I couldn't sleep. My mind kept replaying the evening. What a strange evening it turned out to be. And what a strange feeling it gave me.

I could feel his muscles rapidly surrender as he edged toward sleep. Within a few minutes, Wes was out. I could tell by his heavy breathing and the way he periodically twitched as if he were fighting in his dreams.

Years of pent-up sexual frustration and discontentment for life in general spun inside me like a furious hurricane. Listening to Wesley's life stories—all of the adventures he lived, the improbable social connections he forged, the important lessons he learned—made me feel like my life was nowhere close to where I wanted it to be, despite the fact I worked so hard to get there. It didn't seem fair that I had "played by the rules" all my life only to sink in a tsunami of yearning.

Something uncanny happened inside me as I lay there pondering it all. A dim realization hidden in the recesses of my mind started emerging into the light, but I could only see it faintly. It seemed to suggest I'd been doing almost everything wrong. That my life, even with all of my good intentions, was somehow upside down.

It's not that I wanted a life like Wes's. Not at all. The conversion from number crunching to bone crunching was definitely not in my emotive capacity. But there was something about him I wanted. And I promise, it was more than just lust. There was a particular aura about him. A calm, assured, and peaceful energy that was remarkably pleasant to be around. It attracted me to him on a different level.

Also, his fearless approach to things inspired me. When I commented on how life-threatening some of his experiences were, he replied without skipping a beat,

"Oh well. If I die, I know I've lived a good life. No matter what, it'll be fine."

This made me think: *If I die, I'll feel like my life was cut short and that I missed out on so many things.* Like most young people, I was not ready to die. But Wes, even a little younger than me, almost looked forward to the "adventure on the other side." That's not to imply he wanted to die or was reckless with his life. He simply was not afraid of dying because of the way he had chosen to live. I was afraid of dying because I had not lived, not the way I wanted to anyhow.

As if through osmosis—just being near him, touching him, being mysteriously enveloped in his aura—a divine paradigm started shifting inside me. The tectonic plates of my bosom faulted, creating mountains of positive energy that started in my heart and reverberated throughout my entire being. The process left my chest thumping. I felt inexplicably invigorated at the thought of actually changing my life. It was as though I had just discovered another woman inside of me, someone waiting to slip out.

In a weird, celebratory, subconscious-like state, I embraced him and inhaled the silky skin of his neck. It smelled clean and sharp, like the air after a rainstorm. I thought, admittedly sort of strangely, that he smelled the way a baby bunny felt, something you were inclined to run your hands over and then press to your face. His scent intoxicated me, overwhelmed my better intentions, seduced me so thoroughly that there was no choice to be made. All of my senses slipped away in a rushing current of desire.

At the first touch of his lips, a shudder of satisfaction shivered through me that stopped my breath. And without meaning to, I caved to my carnal cravings. I started unbuttoning his flannel shirt. I had no control over my hands.

"If you take my shirt off, I'm gonna take your shirt off," he hissed a hot threat in my ear. His hand gently moved up my shirt and cupped the softness of the skin under my breast, firebombing shrapnel through my senses. I could not think; I could only feel. And I had never felt that way before. I felt fragmented in his hands and then remade. Lost, and then found. It was as though I had uncovered a whole new world, and yet, on the contrary, like I was coming home to a place I'd always known.

Every cell in my body tingled with anticipation ... and hope. The sensations were so much more than purely of the flesh. They were everything: emotional, biochemical, even spiritual. Our bodies connected and moved sinuously together like a seductive dance that had been rehearsed since before time.

The intensity of our passion quickly overcame me. My nails bit into his back as I climaxed in a way I thought impossible. Every fiber of my body fired and flexed in a stupor of ecstasy, including my vocal chords. Involuntary moans of pleasure slipped through my lips. I hardly recognized the sounds escaping me.

Chapter 5

Around 6:00 a.m. my internal alarm clock summoned me from my dreams. Ruger slept draped over my head like a puffy set of earmuffs. He always did that, making a nest of my hair. Nelli slept flattened like a pancake under the bed. I ever so smoothly picked Ruger up and resettled him to the side of me so Wes would not wake to the spectacle of me wearing a ridiculous, fat, and furry cat hat.

I repositioned myself and turned on my side, away from Ruger, facing Wesley. He slept flat on his back, lightly snoring with both hands resting on his chest. Eventually he rolled toward me, the tip of his nose nearly touching the tip of mine. He was so close his features lost their distinction. All I could see were the startling, staggering feelings I already had for him.

His warm breath on my lips felt as intimate as a kiss. I wanted to bottle how happy I felt in that moment so I could drink of it later when I knew loneliness and sorrow would leave me painfully parched.

After some time, he lazily opened his eyes and peacefully gazed at me before he faintly tilted his head upward and kissed me softly for a long time, like it was our last kiss. His teeth grazed over my bottom lip just before he pulled away. A wave of melancholy washed over me as I realized he was preparing to say goodbye.

I involuntarily held my breath as I watched him slowly collect his scattered clothes. I could tell by the way he moved, he had no lack of confidence in his nudity. His features appeared as though someone had carved them with a keen and clever blade. He looked like a Greek god, and he pompously knew it. Envy cropped up inside me. I wished I felt that comfortable in my own naked skin.

There came a "thud, thud, thud" from under the bed. We both chuckled as Nelli comically wiggled her way out by army-crawling on her stomach, hind legs stretched out flat behind her like a swimming frog.

He kissed me on the forehead, said a quick goodbye, let Nelli out the back door and himself out the front. Just like that, he was gone.

I got up, used the restroom and caught a glimpse of myself in the mirror. Tufts of hair shot out from my head in all directions, like I'd been cow-licked by a drunken bull. I pulled it up into a messy bun, washed my face and debated going into the office, a fairly normal weekend occurrence for me. I'd been working weekends for years even though I hated it. The determination to advance my career as quickly as ethically possible drove me to work hundreds of billable hours over the standard budget identified in my annual compensation package.

In nearly every large public accounting firm across the country, there exists a cultural expectation that top performers will exceed the standard billable budget. Obviously this practice makes top performers more valuable assets since they contribute to the bottom line more than other employees. Adhering to this hard-working expectation was how I personally excused becoming lazy in nearly every other facet of my life.

Because I worked so many hours, I decided I didn't have time to shop for groceries, let alone time to prepare healthy meals for myself. I ate out so frequently the drive-thru employees at Taco Bell knew me by name. Because I worked so many hours, I justified consuming Mountain Dew and coffee in ungodly quantities in order to synthetically maintain the energy necessary to work more hours. Most days began with two tall coffees loaded with cream and sugar followed in the afternoon by three Mountain Dews, and if that didn't do it, I would add a Red Bull to the mix. Because I worked so many hours, I refused to waste the enjoyment of my precious free time by exercising. The most I would do is take Nelli for a walk at the park right out my front door just so I could quiet my nagging conscience. Because I worked so many hours, I stopped making time for family and friends. I stopped making time for all relationships, even my relationship with God. When I wasn't working, Sundays were my day, not the Lord's.

I sensed my priorities starting to shift that morning as I made the decision not to work. I swiftly cleaned the house in preparation for several showings scheduled that day. I let Ruger outside so he could spend the day with his best friend, the bizarre neighbor cat I liked to call Señor Don Gato because of the Spanish-looking mustache his unique coloring gave him, along with his sassy little attitude. Next, I loaded Nelli in my car and headed for my parents' place forty-five minutes away.

Nelli loved to run along the wide-open dirt roads near the small town where my parents lived. I slowly drove behind her as she bounded from one ditch to the next, hysterically searching for rabbits, prairie dogs, birds, mice, and anything else she might chase. She looked back at me in a way that requested approval to jump in the half-frozen ditch water. An adorable puppy smile stretched from one floppy ear to the next. At the sight of her delight, a shadow of guilt loomed within me like a stalking predator. I knew I needed to make more time for her. She deserved it.

As she capered like a fox on the hunt in the tall grass adjacent to the ditch, my mind ceaselessly replayed my date with Wesley. I physically squirmed behind the wheel, dreadfully struggling to clear my mind of him. I shook my head like a dog shakes rain off its fur, trying to free the thoughts that fluttered in my mind like trapped birds. It was useless. "So much for one harmless date," I mocked myself out loud.

I wrestled with the mixed emotions besieging me. My heart and mind played a mean game of tug-of-war. A part of me regretted sleeping with him. I felt a little trashy being a woman who dropped her panties on a first date. What did that say about me? That I'm slutty? Cheap? On the other hand, a part of me was grateful for the unforgettable experience and for learning definitively that my body was not broken.

I wanted it both to be real and an illusion. If it were real, then magic existed. If it were an illusion, then I wouldn't have to figure out how to let it go. Now that I knew the magic, there was no way I could un-know it—and there was no way I could keep it. He was leaving.

I hated that this otherwise beautiful memory would be suffused with sadness, steeped in a sense of having lost what I'd just found.

I wanted to make light of the evening, like I was sure he was doing. He was evidently entirely capable of moving on from a fun fling. I wondered if he thought of me at all or if our date was just like all of the other one-night stands he enjoyed. Was I merely another conquest, a way to love himself through another's body?

Thinking about it so much felt like a waste of my precious free time. *It's not like my thoughts are gonna change anything.*

I tried to focus my attention on appreciating the day with my mom, who is very aptly named Carolyn, which means "song of happiness." My mom plays the guitar, piano, flute, and clarinet. She sings and plays the piano (or sometimes the guitar) every weekend at the Catholic church across the street from the home in which I grew up. She even composes her own music and has written very special and personalized songs for her children for various occasions. For instance, she most recently composed and performed a touching song for my oldest brother Sam's wedding to Lucy.

The best thing about my mom is how she radiates happiness everywhere she goes, which occasionally confounds me, considering the hardships she's endured. I often tease her about the rose-colored glasses she constantly wears, but secretly I envy her ability to see good in all things and give everyone the benefit of the doubt, even if it does come off as naive.

There are few things that soothe my soul like a good conversation with her. She is my role model, uplifter, finest friend, biggest supporter, and probably the person who understands me best. Of course my mom gathered something was bothering me as soon as I arrived, but I avoided talking about Wesley and blamed it on work, an easy and partially true scapegoat. My mom and I talk about everything, but I didn't have the inner strength to voice my jumbled thoughts at that time. I wanted to relax on my rare day off, not spend it performing mental gymnastics.

Later that night, on my way home, I received a text from Wes that read, "Hi, Mila. I had a very nice time on our date together. ☺"

My heart handsprang into my throat. I quietly hoped he would contact me but assumed he wouldn't. I mean, what was the point? He was only home for a little while. I didn't want a long-distance relationship with him and, because of his job, I was sure he wouldn't want one with me. I tried to push my excitement aside. I figured he sent that generic, polite text to every woman he successfully wooed.

I waited until I got home to respond to his message. As a consequence, by the time I got home, my hand hurt from clamping the gearshift like an iron claw, physically restraining myself from responding right away. I blandly replied, "I had a nice time, too," making an effort to dilute my enthusiasm. Within a minute, I received another text from him.

"Any chance you wanna meet again before I go home?"

A surge of revulsion rushed through me. I was exasperated with myself for the decision I knew I was about to make. My heart pounded so hard my hand pulsated slightly as I pressed the send button. "Sure. I'm available tomorrow night."

The eagerness of my irresponsible heart hastily trampled the pragmatic path my mind unavailingly attempted to preserve. The pattern I established of falling for unavailable men needed to be broken. It seemed like every relationship I had came with some sort of caveat that prevented us from truly being together. There was always a catch. The catch in my most recently ended love affair was long distance. He lived in California and was pursuing a career in minor league baseball. In the end, distance won and I lost.

How could I be so giddy and gleeful at the suggestion of seeing Wes again? What was I, some kind of glutton for impossible romances? Trying to tame my raw emotions seemed to only power the cosmic carnival ride taking over inside me. Again, my heart and mind mercilessly teeter-tottered between cool reason and hot passion.

Chapter 6

Wes rang the doorbell at exactly 7:00 p.m. As soon as I opened the door, he pulled me close by the small of my back and whispered, "Hi, beautiful." The warmth of his breath on my lips organically cajoled me forward for a kiss. Not just any kiss, though—the kind of kiss that ignites firecrackers in your belly, that leaves your extremities quivering with delight, that brings a reflexive purr of pleasure to your throat. The kind of kiss that takes you to another place. The kind you might cynically believe only exists in the make-believe world of books and movies.

All of the built-up nerves and negativity mounting inside of me dissolved in that quixotic moment. Illogically, that kiss, lasting only seconds, somehow made up for the hours of dissonance leading up to it.

Our second date confirmed the validity of my initial feelings for him. What I had felt two nights before wasn't just the heat of the moment. It was still there. It was real, and words only limit me when trying to accurately depict the sensations I experienced in his presence. It is like trying to explain something when the knowing can only be understood in the experiencing.

Tell me, what words exist to describe the feelings of a mother the first time she holds her newborn child? The first time a blind man beholds the face of his beloved? Or standing for the first time on a mountain you've conquered? Throughout history people have been searching for words that describe these sensations, but our words can only create a glimpse of that picture through dark, opaque glass. One can never truly understand it until it is personally experienced.

My long-standing doubts about the impossibility of some sort of inexplicable, otherworldly energy mysteriously felt in the presence of another were finally laid to rest. The enigmatic vibe was there. It was real. And there was no explaining it or denying it. It took me by complete surprise. Love will do that, you know. Love will take you by surprise.

I suspected Wes could feel it, too. I sensed it in the heat of his touch. I savored it in the sweetness of his kiss. I saw it in the fervency of his eyes like a cosmic flicker of recognition. His body language snitched on him. It told me things his mouth wouldn't say.

Even Nelli and Ruger seemed at peace. Curled up together on the black rug I had placed specifically with them in mind, they soaked up the warmth of the fire. We ordered delivery from my favorite Asian restaurant and spent the entire evening swept away in a pseudo dreamland where conversation flowed naturally and every touch was energized with the spark of young love.

I had never been that way before—slow-witted and languorous, dreamy, sort of scatterbrained, focused only on each moment as it came. All of me, my mind, body, and soul lived in that present moment, an unfamiliar luxury for someone classically trained in the black art of repetitively examining history and forecasting the future, as was my innate propensity and what my profession required.

As the sun peeked its bright border above the horizon, splashing light across our naked bodies like melted butter, I relaxed serenely in the comfy cocoon of his arms. He laced his fingers between mine before asking, "Will you come over to my parents' house for dinner tonight?" His thumb gently stroked the palm of my hand.

"It's my last night in town, and my mom's cooking a family meal."

The request took me off guard. I definitely did not expect to meet his family, and although I did not ask, I assumed he did not regularly bring girls home to his parents. In this circumstance, there was really no point to it. Meeting someone's family usually comes with the general understanding that you are at a minimum dating with the overall intention of becoming a couple, but usually even more than that, that you are already a serious couple. We were neither. And current conditions dictated we would remain so.

Nevertheless, I wasn't ready to let go. I didn't want to say my final goodbye right then. It was too much. Dinner with his family, though probably a little awkward, would give me another chance to be with him, so I grabbed it.

"Sure," I feebly replied, while momentarily fixating on the thought of him vanishing in less than 24 hours.

Later that evening, I approached the entrance of his parents' property. An attractive white picket fence with large brick pillars bordered the dormant alfalfa fields that ran along the open country roads. A heavy iron gate prohibited me from driving down the long driveway. I rang the call bell. Wes's voice came across the intercom. "Hi, babe."

"Hi, sorry I'm a little late."

"No worries. See you shortly." The gate slowly opened. I drove over the cattle guard and trailed the partially frozen canal lined with cottonwood trees down the curvy private road. About a mile down, I met a fork in the road. One direction led to what I supposed was his parents' house, a large stone cottage, and the other to what I figured was a guesthouse or perhaps a rental property, a simple modular home. I turned between the brick pillars that sat at the entrance of the large circular driveway in front of the main house and parked my car under the frosted branches of a deep-rooted walnut tree.

Oddly, a nervous energy bubbled in my belly. These sorts of things never made me nervous. Although people skills are not generally associated with accountants, years of public speaking at professional training seminars made me an outlier in this respect. Social gatherings usually provided me the opportunity to shine among other talented colleagues.

I surveyed my surroundings and could see more than I anticipated. The bright full moon lit up the crystal-clear country sky, casting haunting shadows of naked trees like skeleton hands shoved up from the underworld. A great horned owl was perched in the tree above the hood of my car calmly staring at me with his yellow eyes. I was drawn to a movement near the horse barn at the edge of the yard where an old Arabian horse observed me through the gate. There was no question about it. WeatherBee Ranch was absolutely breathtaking in the moonlight.

I mentally prepared myself to exit the vehicle. I took a few deep breaths and finally got out of my car. Wes appeared out of nowhere. He ushered me in toward a gazebo laced in white twinkly lights with a stone fire pit in the center. A hot tub sat off to the west looking out toward a snow-capped mountain range that looked like jagged white teeth along a jawbone. Beyond the gazebo, the reflection of the massive moon danced rhythmically on a small pond. The silvery reflection illuminated the sleeping garden nestled nearby in a little valley.

We stepped into a covered porch, removed our shoes, and entered the house. We passed a fireplace bordered by two leather chairs situated near a lovely antique grand piano as we entered the kitchen area.

Dinner with his family developed into a picturesque scene. His mother, a kind, beautiful, intelligent, and optimistic woman, prepared a homemade feast while sipping a glass of red wine. She remembered me from elementary school when she served as my principal for a couple of years before she transitioned to another local school district.

"You've grown up into such a lovely young woman," she pleasantly commented as we exchanged greetings. "Wes tells me you're a successful accountant now," she effortlessly started conversation while commanding various culinary and hosting responsibilities. The signs of a perfectionist were everywhere. I instantly identified with Birdie Blackwell, and I could tell she felt the same about me.

I knew Wes's second-oldest brother, Cole, from high school. He and my older brother, Sam, were classmates and friends. But more than that, Cole was the first boy I ever kissed. I wondered if Wes knew that. It's not like it mattered because it was so many years ago, but I was curious if he knew about it, nonetheless.

It was a kiss I will never forget, mainly because it was my first real kiss, and it shocked the hell out of me. I was only in junior high at the time, but Cole, being a more mature sophomore, skipped right past a peck on the lips and hurtled into a deep-throat French kiss at the end of our first date. I did not enjoy the surprise. Being a total prude and knowing nothing about tonsil hockey, I found the whole thing pretty shocking and gross.

I chose not to go on a second date with Cole, which dumbfounded all of my girlfriends because they thought he was "totally hot." As it turned out, Cole ended up dating nearly every one of my close girlfriends over the course of our high school years. My best friend dated him for a good stretch of time, so I got to know him pretty well.

I had not talked to Cole for many years, but I could immediately tell the rumors about his PTSD were true. He didn't look like himself. Once a wildly handsome man, now he appeared depressed and was overweight.

He looked like a man suffering from some kind of emotional haunting. Pain transformed his features, reshaped his expression into one of forbidding despondency. I could see the drug abuse in his pupils and shaky hands. I could actually smell the funk of hopelessness that clung to his dirty clothing. A surge of sadness rose up and crashed over me. Seeing him like that nearly broke my heart in two.

I guess having to live with the man inside him who had to do the things that needed to be done—who saw the things that had to be seen—during his time in war, left him injured in its own terrifying way. Cole may have come home from the war, but he didn't really come back. Everywhere he went, he took a dark shadow with him, one cast internally but seen unmistakably through his eyes, now sunken in their sockets.

I learned that night that Cole had become a recluse years ago. I suppose he thought that if he could only get far enough away from everyone that time might do its job in healing him. Yet, from what I could see, this method only seemed to yank him further down into a deep, black crater of despair.

Seeing Cole like that, barely carrying on a life somewhere within the craggy confines of the thing we civilians really have no good name for, affected me deeply. It made my heart hurt tremendously. I thought about how unfair it was that war should be allowed to hollow out a man's core like that. It also made me fear Wes might get

to that point someday, that something in his future service might break him like it did his brother.

Regardless of Cole's gloomy presence, a fact of life
his family had seemingly become accustomed to, laugh-
ter and the appealing aroma of old-fashioned home
cooking filled the dining room. Wes's dad, Henry, led a
heartfelt prayer before dinner was served. Following
their familial tradition, we all held hands as Henry genuinely thanked God for bringing us together. There was
something distinct in the tone of his voice that conveyed
his deep appreciation for the evening, and I found it very
touching.

Unlike with my family, it was somewhat of a rarity
for the Blackwell family to be gathered under one roof.
My family congregated nearly every Sunday, but with
two of the Blackwell boys deploying shortly after high
school and the third settling more than an hour away in
the refuge of the Colorado mountains, family get-to-
gethers proved difficult to arrange. Will, the oldest son
of the three, the one whom I had never met, could not
make it to dinner that night. Nevertheless, I could tell
by the tone of Henry's prayer that the evening was special to him, and the look in Birdie's eyes exhibited an
identical sentiment. I hoped I was not intruding on their
rare family moment.

Even though it was cold outside, Wes grilled some of
their homegrown Black Angus beef. It was the best beef
I'd ever tasted. When I commented on it, Henry puffed

up with pride as he told me how they had a special way of feeding out their steers before they were butchered and how they aged the hanging meat longer than most, which made the beef especially tender and tasty. Subsequently, I also learned why Wes had ordered salmon on our first date, even though he took me to a steakhouse. He and his other family members had become so spoiled by their own beef that all other beef was unsatisfactory, even if ordered from a decent restaurant.

After the meal, Wes leaned over and crooned in my ear, "Stay with me tonight." A string of shivers shot down my spine. Although I felt awkward sleeping with him in the thin-walled bedroom across the hallway from his parents' bedroom, I didn't hesitate to accept his bidding. It was our last night together, and all feelings of awkwardness ranked subordinate to the irrefutable feeling that I must seize the fleeting moment.

It's truly astounding the extent of communication that can transpire through touch alone. Even though we had not exchanged the words "I love you," the powerful emotion was palpable in every caress, kiss, and hot breath. The words burned inside me, aching to be given voice. But I had just gotten to know him and knew that I would lose him in a handful of hours. I was afraid it would hurt more somehow if I declared myself to him.

We struggled to hush the sounds of our passion. The joint effort of quietness combined with the tragic brevity of time only amplified the intensity of desire passing between us. His hands expertly moved over every square inch of my body, awakening the butterflies in the fissure of my torso and leaving my skin prickling all over.

He tangled his fingers in my long hair and covered my mouth with his own when noises sought to liberate from deep within me. I know it sounds like an exaggeration, but making love to him that night somehow transported me from my earthly plane of reality to a brand-new plane of pure wonderment.

Morning approached abruptly. I dreaded saying goodbye. It was unclear to me whether or not I would see him again in the next year ... or ever. He walked me to the front door and tightly embraced me, drawing back with reluctance I could feel. "I'm going to miss you," I vulnerably admitted. I couldn't be sure, but I thought something in his eyes confessed he felt the same.

His body faintly trembled before he suddenly strengthened and responded in an oddly measured tone. "It'll be fine, Mila."

Curiously, whatever I identified in his eyes just seconds before, changed. His eyes no longer confessed what I thought was the mutual feeling of longing. I wished I knew him well enough to read the look in his eyes. Was it sadness? Worry? Pain? No. Those were the emotions filling *my* eyes, the emotions that made sense to me when saying goodbye, possibly forever, to the best thing my hands had ever held.

I wasn't sure what emotion filled his eyes, but if I didn't know any better, I'd say whatever it was, was almost entirely the opposite of what filled mine. It was something more akin to tranquility.

I said my final goodbye with a smile, though all the blood in my body seemed to have stopped running. His sheer serenity in what should have been a moment of emotional unrest confused and even chafed at me. Perhaps he was just keeping it together for my benefit, but I doubted it. It seemed more like he engaged a kind of "mission mode" that allowed him to fearlessly move forward no matter what presented itself in the path before him.

I waited until my back was turned before I allowed big, stinging tears to veil my vision. And as I walked away from him toward my car, the cold feeling of loneliness blew like a biting wayward wind across my tear-streaked face.

Chapter 7

Feeling all mixed up inside, I called my childhood best friend and kindred spirit, Gracelyn. Gracie, though she tries hard to disguise it, has this ginormous, out-of-control heart that seems to get her in more trouble than good. It was nice to be near it, though, especially because sometimes I could scarcely make out my own heart amid the clamor of my hyperactive brain. I asked her to meet me for lunch.

"So what's the latest 'n' greatest in your life?" She jovially inquired as she plopped in the restaurant booth.

I sat down jadedly, tucking one foot under me. My heart swelled up with misery until it felt too large to fit in my ribcage. My hands became icy, and a feeling of tragedy oppressed me. "Oh, you mean other than falling madly in love with yet another unavailable man?" I replied with a vexed, mordant tone.

"Again?! Oh geez ... " She eyeballed me with a look of censure, kindly blended with pity. "Well, gimme the scoop," she patiently waited for me to start talking while we perused the menu. When I didn't say anything right away, she looked up from the menu and noticed water brimming in my eyes. I rarely, if ever, cried in public, and my genuine sadness stunned her into compassion. "Oh, honey," she said tenderly. "Why're you crying? Who is this jerk?"

"I don't even know where to start," I dolefully answered, while trying to choke back a torrent of tears. "It's different this time, Grace. I've never felt this way before." I took a sip of my drink, hoping it might tamp down the ache in my chest.

"Do I know him?" she asked.

"Yes ... " I hesitated, almost embarrassed to admit the once dorky little twerp from high school somehow managed to twist my world upside down. "Cole's younger brother, Wes."

"Wes the Fucking Mess! No way. Are you shittin' me?!" She amusingly reacted. "I see what you're talkin' about, though. Gaaaaaaaawd, he grew up into quite the dreamboat, didn't he!" Gracie was my best friend I mentioned earlier who dated Cole for a couple of years, so she knew the Blackwell family pretty well. "Is he still active duty in the Navy?"

"Yes. That's the problem, you see. I don't know when, or if, I'll ever see him again. We spent a little time over Christmas together while he was home on leave." I paused before adding, "You know me, Grace. I've never been a believer in love at first sight. I've always been much too pragmatic for that kinda feathery concept."

Gracie laughed in a good-hearted way and nudged me from across the table with her pointer finger. "And now you're a believer?" A ridiculous smile conveyed the thought she was too kind to say. She wanted to, but didn't say, "I told you so."

I grabbed her hand and threw it back at her playfully. "Yes," I grumbled, clearly bedeviled by the happenstance. I used to shake my head when people talked about falling in love quicker than Cupid's speeding arrow. *Poor deluded folk*, I presumed. I figured they were grasping at some preternatural idyll not intended for mere mortals but that sounded very lovely in a poem. Then along came Wes, and I, the cynic, became the converted.

"Hmmm," she thought for a moment. "I wish I could be a voice of encouragement for you, Mila, but you know what the military did to Cole and me." She pursed her lips, disguising a grimace. "I know firsthand that dating someone in the military is damn near impossible. You have to have a lot of trust, that's for sure. Personally, I couldn't handle not seeing him for months at a time. There'd be weeks in a row when I couldn't even get in touch with him because of whatever he was doing during his deployment. I felt like I was dating a ghost." I nodded at her somberly because I remembered all too well her struggle with that. Mine was often the shoulder she leaned on during that time.

She continued, "I waited so long for him to come back home, and when he finally did, he was different ... or we were. We tried to patch things up, but we had grown too far apart. I didn't see him as the man I fell in love with anymore. He seemed guarded and deeply disturbed by experiences he wouldn't, or couldn't, talk about. Our lines of communication were ... " She considered her words briefly before finally finishing, " ... well, we'll just say, they were seriously fucked up."

"Wow, you're right. That wasn't helpful at all," I said. We both snorted a half-laugh.

"You never know, Mila. That was my experience. It doesn't have to be yours. You started dating Wes after he became a military man. I knew Cole before. I think maybe it makes a difference."

"Thanks, hon. Truthfully, this whole conversation is probably for naught. I don't want another long distance relationship and I doubt he'd want one, either. And like you said, a handful of dates is obviously no foundation for that kind of relationship."

She nodded her head. "You're probably right. It requires a lot of trust, and you can't build that in just a few dates. That being said, I'm not surprised you two hit it off. You're nothing alike but exactly the same, if you know what I mean." I raised an eyebrow in confusion. I didn't know what she meant. When I asked, she simply laughed at her cryptic message, not offering follow-up clarification.

"Do you know how Birdie is, by the way?" She suddenly changed topics as though something had popped into her head. The tone of her voice and the way she asked me seemed a bit peculiar, but I didn't take the cue.

"I had dinner with his family last night. Birdie's such a sweetheart! She's so easy to talk to."

"Yeah, she is," Gracie agreed. "I love her. So, she seemed healthy then?"

"What do you mean? She seemed very healthy."

Realizing we were not on the same page, Gracie explained, "You know she was diagnosed with colon cancer like five years ago, don't you? It's a miracle she's still alive."

My jaw hit the floor. I had no idea. *Why wouldn't Wesley mention something like that?* Thinking back, no one in his family had alluded to her health at dinner.

"No. I didn't know that," I said slowly, trying to digest the news.

"As far as I know, they tried to treat it, but they weren't able to remove all of the cancer cells," she proceeded to explain. "Last I heard, she had surgery to remove the cancer and then had radiation and, I think, chemo. However, the cancer came back and spread to other parts of her body. I think her lungs and maybe her brain. I'm not sure. That's all I know."

This sad news punched me like an invisible person right in the gullet. I tried to catch my breath. My heart pumped blood at the rate of an Olympic skier as an avalanche of thoughts rendered me speechless. *What an incredible woman she must be to uphold such a positive and peppy attitude while battling the second-deadliest cancer known to man. How could Wes even consider extending his service with his mother being so sick?*

The news of Birdie's cancer genuinely affected me. There I sat, healthy as a horse, despite my daily efforts to destroy my health, yet I couldn't seem to wrangle a positive outlook to save my life. I suddenly felt very selfish and ungrateful.

I knew over the past decade I had progressively slipped into a nasty habit of taking for granted all the blessings in my life. I recognized my error but couldn't seem to navigate my attitude away from the negative fog that clouded my dreary world. The idea of actual change was daunting. The more entrenched in my unhealthy, unhappy habits I became, the less inclined I was to believe anything else was worth the effort, if even possible. The path seemed too distant, too difficult, too rocky, and too risky—the excuses went on and on. Familiar routines, even though frequently dissatisfying, at least had their own predictability. To live my life at the caliber I truly desired required extreme changes that were saturated in unpredictability. I never felt equipped with enough time, energy, or courage to face those changes ... especially not alone, which is how I felt even in the company of most others.

The people I spent the most time with throughout the week were work friends, not real friends—people I got along with very well but didn't allow into my personal bubble beyond a professional extent. I resolved to be cheerful and nice to everyone so the partners would see me as someone with people skills. I was determined and ever in pursuit of professional advantages. This often obliged a gregarious presence: eye contact, big smiles, and friendly handshakes, not because of any real consideration, but because every work relationship potentially held value in positioning me for greater achievement.

The disgusting truth of the matter is that I understood the value of kindness as a means to more lucrative objectives; after all, people who care about you are much easier to influence, and the easiest way to get people to care about you is to care about them, or at least appear to. Therefore, I made a lot of "friends," yet my life remained sorely lonesome. Other than my family and Gracie, I didn't make time for real friendships. Actually caring was an emotional extravagance for which I had no time or energy after exhausting all that I had on other priorities.

Ever since college, I had teetered on the brink of depression. I'm not sure if it was indeed depression or simply suffering from some grisly side effect of putting unreasonable performance pressure on myself. The more achievements I hoarded, the more I raised the bar of performance expectations, and failure to meet them was never an option. And this, of course, was not limited to academia. The more compliments I received on my appearance, the more I elevated the bar of beauty expectations. The more popular I became, the higher I set the bar of social expectations. After a while, there were a lot towering bars, too many, in fact, for me to live up to.

Realistically, though, whatever was going on with me emotionally was probably related to a combination of many things. To name just a few others: going from working out every day to never working out, eating unhealthily, losing my faith in many ways, and, no doubt, drug abuse.

I did a remarkable job hiding the symptoms of my depression from other students, coworkers, friends and family. For example, most people who knew me would never in a million years suspect I smoked pot several times a day just to get through it. All of those years of keeping my nose jammed in books and never missing Sunday mass had apparently given me some kind of goody-two-shoes force field. People assumed I was principled and virtuous and never suspected anything less of me. I was committed to keeping my condition concealed, so I used my force field on a daily basis to whitewash my life in the eyes of others, effortlessly covering up the dark truth.

I knew in my core there was no valid excuse for me to feel the way I did, so I didn't want others to know about it. Looking in from the outside, I had it all: a full-ride scholarship, beauty, a close-knit family, a handsome boyfriend. What more could one want?

Leading one life on the outside but experiencing a different life on the inside was an awfully isolating practice. It was also tiresome. The superhuman effort it sometimes took to appear normal and a part of things that were easy and everyday, exhausted me.

I justified my marijuana usage because I never felt that it barred me from succeeding in academics or my career. In fact, I passed all four of the CPA exams high as kite, on the first attempt, too. There was only one other person in my department who had passed all four of the exams on the first attempt, and I guarantee she was stone sober. It generally took two, if not three, attempts to pass some of the exams. The smartest partner I knew had to take one of the exams four times before passing, so I felt I was doing all right. Heck, better than all right. I was killing it.

So I got stoned every day before work and on my lunch break. I basically maintained a high uninterrupted by sobriety and still remained the top performer of my peer group. Thus, I believed my marijuana usage was inconsequential, and it was the only thing that made my tedious days bearable.

When I think back to how my drug abuse started, it all boiled down to anger, disappointment, and resentment. The areas of my life where I worked the hardest and sacrificed the most led me nowhere, or at least not to happiness. I worked hard in all of my romantic relationships and always ended up heartbroken and alone. I worked hard in my career and ended up unsatisfied. I worked hard at my connection with God and felt like He disappeared when I needed Him most. For being such a "successful" woman, I felt like a total failure.

Most of my anger, disappointment, and resentment were pointed at God. It was easier than directing it at myself. I never stopped believing in Him, but I certainly stopped believing in His loving nature. I think this is from where my loneliness and hopelessness truly stemmed. The whole world seemed harsh and unfair, not just toward me but everyone, and I couldn't understand how a loving God, capable of all things, could allow such appalling things to happen, especially to people with good hearts and pure intentions.

The seed of my personal resentment first burrowed into the soil of my soul the night I discovered sex was painful for me. I saved myself, as challenging as it was, for a man I cared deeply about, and sex ended up being the foremost reason why our relationship crumbled to despair.

During the years I tried to improve my sex life with Oliver, things only worsened. For the longest time I refused to believe our situation was unfixable. I thought that with a little hard work and determination and, by all means, the assistance of capable doctors, we could fix it and make everything better. It truly befuddled me when I finally came to the realization that things were never going to get better, despite our best efforts. And with absolute bewilderment, like that of a pampered child who had always gotten her own way and who now, for the first time, was in contact with the unpleasantness and unfairness of life, I began to close God out.

I thought perhaps I was being punished for not saving myself until marriage, and in my mind, the punishment did not fit the crime. Not even close. I was only trying to love Ollie. And even if I wasn't being punished, how could God withhold one of life's most amazing gifts from me? It wasn't fair. This was how He repaid me for a lifetime of trying to be a good person? Because up until that point, I really had tried to make the right choices.

Sure, I admit some of my choices were selfish, specifically when it came to my quest for success, but I was never a vicious person. There wasn't a malicious bone in my body. I may have put myself before others when I shouldn't have, but I never specifically set out to hurt anyone, ever. In fact, I tried my best to avoid it if I could. Only when competition demanded I step on someone's toes did I do it. It's not like I enjoyed it. And believe me, I had my own toes stepped on plenty of times in the process.

Up until that point, I had never taken drugs. I could count the number of times I'd been drunk on one hand. I didn't skip class. I prayed every single day. I helped others when I could. I was essentially the epitome of a good girl with good grades and a bright future. I didn't deserve to be treated that way. It wasn't fair.

Tell me, how could I ever expect to be in a healthy relationship without being able to enjoy sex? Scratch that. It wasn't just not being able to enjoy it. Sex was downright painful. It would rip and scar my most sensitive and tender skin. Do you know any decent man who would want to feel as though he were raping his loved one when only trying to physically show his love and desire for her? No? I didn't think so. You see, it wasn't just about sex. Not only was enjoyable sex taken from me, but more importantly, the precious gift of a healthy, lasting romantic love was torn away with it. How could God do that to me?

I had taken big risks to be closer to Him, too. The biggest risk involved leaving the Catholic faith, which I felt spiritually called to do. I knew leaving the faith of my family meant losing the respect of my parents and siblings and even my extended family. My parents were distraught to say the very least. It was one of the few times I made my mom cry tears of disappointment. My siblings went so far as to tell me I would not be a god-mother to their unborn children. I risked permanently damaging precious family ties in order to lead the life I felt mystically drawn to.

I know it may seem paradoxical to say I was trying to repair my relationship with God by leaving the Church that helped raise me, but I knew in my heart there were things about the Catholic faith that were holding me back from my spiritual growth. I felt boxed in by the Church. There were too many nonsensical rules and tra-ditions and some beliefs I didn't agree with. My leaving the Church had nothing to do with me abandoning God, like many people assumed. My problems with God stemmed from something entirely separate.

Even though everything eventually improved with my family over time, not being able to improve my inti-macy situation with Ollie caused turmoil in my spiritual world. A seed of bitterness found fertile soil in my soul. What began as a kernel, something that might have been effortlessly washed away by serious reflection, spread roots at every injustice.

Like most things, the encroachment of corruptive thoughts is a gradual process. It doesn't happen overnight. For most of us, the process usually isn't something even obviously malevolent. Or so it was with me. I hardly recognized how the devil, and his silver tongue, easily smooth-talked me into making small adjustments to truth and minor justifications over time that had the effect of poisoning my perception of the world and my experience of it. I discovered the hard way that the inside property of the soul is truly impressive but frighteningly fragile. Allowing weeds to take root, rather than beneficial vegetation, reshaped the landscape of my inner property in unimaginable ways.

After Wes went back to Louisiana, my lonesomeness and hopelessness sank to a new low. In my mind, God was in the horrible habit of playing cruel tricks on me. It seemed as though He loved to dangle the proverbial carrot in front of me, allowing me to get close to it, before ripping it away just when I thought I might be able to catch it. Losing the carrot (Wes) hurt worse this time than before. One might think I'd be hardened to this ill-fated pattern by this point in my life. I was not, though. I was beaten and broken, feeling abused by the One who was supposed to love and protect me most.

The emptiness that threatened to suffocate me after Wes left functioned as the main catalyst in my decision to leave my position at the accounting firm. Profound dissatisfaction stirred my soul to action at last. I no longer felt it was acceptable to throw away my days in an office that created more stress than gratification, no matter the monetary incentive. Also, learning of Birdie's battle with cancer reminded me that life is too short, and I needed to stop wasting my precious time doing things that left me feeling hollow inside.

The partners attempted to entice me to stay after I submitted my resignation, but my decision was irreversible. The intense relief I experienced knowing I wouldn't have to spend another day in that taxing job forbade me from even considering cutting a deal. I worked with an executive career recruiter to find another accounting position that I hoped would better suit my need for a more reasonable work/life balance.

Chapter 8

I started my new job the day after I left the accounting firm. It was a huge risk leaving the firm that had fostered my abilities, especially since I scrupulously developed great working relationships with upper management and all of my clients and was unquestionably on the fast track to success.

Accepting a position with another large corporation, I wondered if I had simply changed lanes in the rat race rather than taking an exit. The first month of my employment, I carefully evaluated my peers and my boss to gain an understanding of the expectations I'd be held to in my new position. Things were not looking good. While there were notable improvements in my day-today responsibilities, the chief purpose of changing jobs—to obtain a healthier work/life balance—fell short of my needs.

While sitting in my office two months later, I received a text from Wes explaining that he had formally extended his contract with the Navy. He told me he received orders to deploy to Panama in late March and would not return until sometime in late October.

Even though I knew upfront he had planned to prolong his service, I'd be lying if I tried to pretend it didn't dishearten me when I received the official news that day. He tried to make light of the situation. "It won't be that bad, Mila. Time moves more quickly than you imagine. Plus you're a strong girl." He said, "It'll be fine."

And there it was again. The phrase he used all the time, "It'll be fine." I cringed at it. I wanted to scream: *It won't be fine! We won't be fine! ...* I *won't be fine.*

"Do you say that about everything?" I texted back, only thinly disguising my irritation.

"What?" He played dumb.

"'It'll be fine.'"

"Haha, yeah, I guess. Everything always is."

He wanted me to consider a long-distance relationship with him. He understood my reservations and thought them trivial in the grand scheme of things. He merely took the stance that if it's meant to be, it'll work out; and if not, then it was worth a shot. He'd never had his heart broken before. I could tell by how casually he addressed the possibility. I, on the other hand, was not anxious to sign myself up for a relationship in which I knew I would end up spending the majority of my time missing the person I wanted to spend my time with most.

In my expert opinion, a future with Wes forecasted poorly. I didn't know if he would extend his contract with the Navy several more times, if he would join a different military branch, or if he would accept high-level security contract work, all of which he talked about and any of which would require him to be gone for significant stints of time.

I ran all of my best and most advanced profitability analyses, taking into consideration the most material data points, and the analyses suggested that a long-distance relationship with him would be like investing my heart in a shitty triple-B-rated bond rather than a secure triple A. Or said another way, it would be about as successful as trying to pick feathers out of molasses.

It truly dumbfounded me that he wanted to be in a relationship when he could easily choose not to be. For a man accustomed to the freedom of engaging in as many one-night stands as he pleased, this choice seemed unusual and even a little suspicious, especially since he'd be gone for six months and, to add to the matter, I had learned he preferred the look of a South American woman to any other. I can't remember exactly how it came up in conversation, but it was made clear to me that he liked dark hair, eyes, and skin, and curvy figures, none of which I had. And knowing this added something new to the mix, a toxic dash of jealousy.

The whole situation spelled certain doom for the impending months. Nevertheless, despite the pit in my stomach and my earnest reservations, I agreed to it. Our success rate was highly suspect, but my heart ultimately grabbed the reins and accepted the risk before my mind had the chance to steer me in a more prudent direction.

Initially he had no plans of coming back to Colorado before he deployed to Panama, but when I finally agreed to a long-distance relationship with him, he decided to visit one week before he deployed. We spent as much time as we could together, which also meant spending a lot of time with his family.

I tried my best to be stoic about the situation. I wanted to display strength, even if I could physically feel my innards unraveling. I disbelieved our amateur stage of affection could endure the long, lonely road ahead, no matter how much we both wanted it. I resigned myself to the likelihood that the distance between us would inevitably poison the tiny love bud incubating in our hearts.

Wes believed the distance would make us stronger. He believed in the value of an intimate letter and thought it was a powerful instrument in getting to know someone. His optimism never swayed, and for that reason, I played along.

He romantically joked, "Trust me, babe. You better enjoy this 'cause there'll come a time when you'll be so sick of me, you'll do anything to get me out of the house!" Hearing him hint at a future with me kindled a chemical reaction in the pit of my stomach, yet I wouldn't tolerate my imagination to entertain the possibility. I dared not explore the happy visual of blissful decades with him that my heart yearned to imagine.

I know he sensed my hesitations. He went out of his way to be tender and encouraging. He even went so far as to suggest we change our status on Facebook to reflect our relationship, which couldn't have been more out of character for him.

Having never explored this profile setting, he was amused by all of the relationship statuses available to choose from and preceded to recommend we select "in a civil union." I opted for the more traditional "in a relationship" status to avoid too many questions from my nosy family.

Birdie must have detected my sensitive state, too, for she gave me her e-mail address and asked for mine. She wanted to keep in touch over Wes's deployment. Call it mother's intuition, but from the very beginning, Birdie recognized something magical taking place, and she felt compelled to nurture it along. She told me in confidence, "I've never seen Wes so enamored before." My eyes glittered with crystals of euphoria. I had never been so enamored before either.

❧

The week passed in a blur of almost unbearable bliss. Sleeping was apparently not on the agenda. The fervor of passion blazed too brightly to allow much shut-eye. We stole short naps between each intimate joining.

Wes possessed the amazing talent of taking me several steps down the evolutionary ladder until I basically became nothing more than a central core with only a tiny trace of a limbic system and cerebral cortex.

"I love how tight you are," he breathed in my ear. This sent vibrations down my backbone that fundamentally concentrated in my lower back, naturally causing my hips and navel to arch skyward. My vaginal muscles pulsated in a way I had never experienced before meeting him. The erotic muscular movement coaxed inward, swallowing him deep inside me.

Even as a former Catholic and inherently prudent person, it is far easier for me to candidly describe the uncontrollable carnalities born out of raw passion than it is to describe the emotional and spiritual components also present. Like I mentioned before, words are limitations when trying to illustrate such things. I'm reluctant to reduce the immensity of such feelings to the inadequacy of my words. The only way I can think to describe it is that being with him gave me an inexplicable sense that I was somehow fulfilling a destiny I signed up for before I merged into the world of being from nonbeing.

Upon waking up our last morning together, I desperately tried to memorize the images before me. The morning sun filled the bedroom, creamy as lemon chiffon, deliciously lighting the curvature of his muscles and the peacefulness of his sleeping face.

I looked at the alarm clock, aglow in the sunlight, and tried to calculate the minutes until I had to say goodbye. Twenty-three.

He awoke in the next five minutes and pulled my naked body on top of his. He confessed, "I could really get used to this." My heart throbbed to the point of bursting. His words teased of a future that would likely never be.

"What's gonna happen to us?" I asked, sounding more pitiful than I would have liked.

He leaned closer, no doubt trying to underscore his words. "I don't know, Mila. The only thing I know for sure is that if we both want it bad enough, we'll find a way to make it work."

I knew it was the only thing he could say, but the question of our future left me unsettled. I didn't say that, though. Instead, I drew a long breath and silently prayed that time would stop somehow.

He delicately cupped my face with his strong hands and kissed me tenderly. He drew back and looked at me. His gaze pierced through me, to the very depth of me. An overwhelming fluttering pain started in my stomach and journeyed to my ribcage. His eyes were so penetrating that anticipation seared my organs and left me feeling queasy and clammy. It was difficult to maintain eye contact with that kind of intensity.

Without blinking, he said, "I love you, Mila." His words seem to settle in the room, soft as snow. A fusion of happy and sad tears pooled in my eyes.

He was saying goodbye.

A single drop from my eye fell on his chest, coincidentally over his heart. He skimmed his soft lips over my misty eyelashes and then hugged me tightly to the nook of his neck. My face naturally nestled up to his neck as though it were the final piece of a jigsaw puzzle.

One of his hands brushed through my hair while the other tickled the small of my back. My throat felt so constricted with sharp, pointy emotions I feared no words could escape. When my voice finally squeezed past the splintery things in my throat, it came out reedy and scratched. "I love you, too," I muttered hoarsely in his ear.

I wished I would've looked into his eyes as I told him I loved him for the first time, but the suffocating weight of already missing him pinned me to his body.

Chapter 9

Subject: Hello from Panama
Sunday, March 24, 2013, at 9:49 PM
To: Mila / From: Wes

Mi amor,

Got in this afternoon and have been busy trying to get settled in ever since. From the sound of things, I'm gonna stay this way for a few weeks until the guys we're replacing down here are able to turn over all of the information to us. Since we're on a "sneaky squirrel" mission the transition needs to be covert and seamless, which can take time. Patience is key.

The living arrangements are decent. We have some apartments that overlook the water. There is a small anchorage closer to shore with plenty of smaller sailboats and then larger commercial ships out in the deeper water. Not a bad view at all, if I say so myself!

We have an average-sized kitchen and just about everything one would need to be comfortable. It's also nice to be working in civilian clothes, boardshorts and flip-flops. Lucky for you, I should come home looking like a bronzed god. ☺

I'm exhausted, so I'm gonna retire and test out this bed. I'm a little nervous due to the fact it feels about as stiff as your bed, along with not having the warmth that accompanies me when I sleep next to you.

I miss you already. Goodnight, beautiful.

Subject: Hello from Colorado
Sunday, March 24, 2013, at 10:53 PM
To: Wes / From: Mila

Wes,

I'm glad you made it to your final destination safely. It's actually kind of romantic picturing you writing me while stowed away in some Panamanian apartment overlooking the water. I'm imagining you shirtless in your boardshorts and flip-flops now ... Yum. ☺

Your living arrangements sound more like a vacation than a deployment. Good for you. Hopefully the "sneaky squirrel" aspect of this deployment makes it less dangerous? Or maybe that's just wishful thinking on my part.

Your mom e-mailed me today. She wants to meet for lunch in a couple of weeks. She told me to invite my mom, too. Boy, will your ears be burning!

I suppose I'll have to cuddle up next to Nelli tonight. Luckily, she drools in her sleep about as much as you do, so the transition should be smooth ... or should I say slobbery?

I miss you more. Sleep tight handsome.

Subject: Buenas noches, bonita
Monday, March 25, 2013, at 9:14 PM
To: Mila / From: Wes

Buenas noches bonita,

Just finishing up with the day. I'm staying very busy with work. It's not exactly the kind of work I'm used to, and I'm still not sure how I feel about it. It does make the day go by with lightning speed, though. And rest assured, what I'm doing at the moment is not very dangerous.

I'm excited to be using my Spanish again. I'm really trying to make the best of this deployment. It might be my last one for a bit.

So I was thinking, you know how you don't put much, if any, effort into your health? Well, I think now is the perfect time to start! Physical fitness and eating right is emphasized in the military not only because of the obvious benefits of building strength and stamina (and looking hot naked), but for the mental and emotional benefits, as well. These kinds of transitions can be very mentally and emotionally demanding. Besides, a little bit of exercise will help you build up that skinny ass of yours. ☺ Don't be mad, you know it's true.

Goodnight, my love.

Subject: Buenos días, guapo
Tuesday, March 26, 2013, at 4:27 AM
To: Wes / From: Mila

Buenos días, mi novio guapo!

I'm glad to hear you're staying busy, although I'm sure you can't wait to find some free time to go scuba diving. How's the water? Are you in a good diving area? I'm not sure how much I can ask you about what you're doing …? I'm naturally very curious, though.

I agree, this transition *is* emotionally demanding. It must be physically demanding, too, considering I fell asleep at seven last night. I haven't gone to bed at that hour since I was a wee one. I'm doing my best to stay strong and be positive, but it's taking every ounce of energy. I'm bone tired and soul weary, but there is no way I can really rest. Life goes on even though it feels like my entire world came to a crashing halt. So thanks for that. ☺

Okay, okay, okay, I will do my best to be more conscientious of my health. Anyhow, I guess now I have to keep up with all of those South American bombshells you speak so highly of. Wes, I'd be lying if I told you it didn't concern me at all—you being so far away from me and simultaneously being surrounded by beautiful women willing to do anything to snag an American man. I can't compete with their naturally curvy bodies, no matter how many squats I do. If it's a big ass you are looking for, you won't find it on me.

Love,
Mila

Subject: Dreaming of you
Tuesday, March 26, 2013, at 4:03 AM
To: Mila / From: Wes

Just wanted to let you know I was dreaming of you all night ...

Subject: Now that I'm awake
Tuesday, March 26, 2013, at 5:58 AM
To: Mila / From: Wes

Okay, now that I'm awake! The water is decent nearby our apartment. The better diving water is about an hour and a half from here. I don't think we'll have time to check it out until this turnover is complete. It's gonna be another long day.

I'm sorry, babe, but I can't tell you anything about what I'm doing. Any information that is leaked about this kind of operation puts everyone at risk. You're lucky to even know I'm in Panama right now. Trust me, I wish I could go into more detail with you due to the comical factor it brings along with the disappointment in how this part of our "empire" works.

I will send you an e-mail before I crash tonight if we make it back to our rooms.

I miss you.

Oh and, Love, try not to worry. I'm not gonna run away with some South American "bombshell." Usually, the only reason they're so desperate to pick up an American man is to get a green card, anyway. I'm looking for something a little more at this point in my life.

And, yes, you *can* achieve a curvy lower body if you work out. Squats, squats, and more squats!

Subject: Fraternizing with the enemy
Tuesday, March 26, 2013, at 4:12 PM

To: Wes / From: Mila

Hey babe,

I'm sitting in my office (a.k.a. my prison cell) completing an investment roll-forward for the auditors. Auditors give me headaches. I work with four different auditing groups and at least three auditors from each group. I work with: 1) auditors for the consolidated results of the parent company; 2) auditors for the standalone results of both insurance companies; 3) auditors for the state of Hawaii where the insurance companies are domiciled; and 4) internal auditors. That is enough auditors to give anyone a migraine!

Did I tell you my house is under contract again? This time I think the buyer is serious. I'm hoping to close in the next couple of weeks. I'll be so relieved when I sell this place. It's been on the market for six months now. Eff this daily vacuuming. LOL! Between Nelli's fat feet leaving perfect paw impressions everywhere and Ruger's black fur, there is no prayer of keeping the carpet show-worthy if I let them inside, which I always do.

Truthfully, though, I'm a little nervous about moving back in with my parents in the interim. It's been nearly a decade since I last lived with them. My dad is not the easiest person to live with.

I've decided to give to my family and donate to Goodwill nearly all of my furniture and most of my belongings so I don't have to put a bunch of things in storage. I don't know what to do with Nelli, though. Her gigantic paws will rip my mom's pristine yard apart if I bring her with me, and that just won't do. My mom's yard is her sanctuary. And knowing the hardship she's dealt with during her life, she deserves a sanctuary. I would feel awful when (not if) Nelli destroyed it.

My heart hurts thinking about it. I love my Smelli (as my two-year-old nephew, Cooper, calls her). I need to figure out a solution soon. Time is running short ... So many changes in such a short period of time.

P.S. I bought multivitamins today. One baby step in a healthy direction!

Love,

Milena Rudenko, CPA
Statutory Accounting Department
R.K.D. Holdings, Inc.
8810 S. Belleview Dr. #600 | Denver, CO 80237
Direct Phone: 751.555.1005 / Ext: 991005 |
milena.rudenko@rkd.com

Subject: Turnovers give me headaches
Tuesday, March 26, 2013, at 10:13 PM

To: Mila / From: Wes

Mi amor,

It's about ten in the evening, and I literally just stepped in the door. Been another long day, and I'll be so glad when this turnover is done. Everyone has their own way of doing things, I suppose ... BUT I happen to think my ideas are far more efficient. ☺ So don't worry, Love, you weren't the only one brewing headaches this afternoon.

Tell me more about your dad. Why isn't he "the easiest person to live with?" I sort of know some of the things that happened when Ben and I were in grade school, but I think we were both too young to really understand it. Ben never talked about it either.

Hmmm ... I kind of like the fact you're gonna give away most of your furniture and belongings, though you might want to proceed with caution. I think I'm rubbing off on you! Technically, I don't own any furniture either. It's all attached to the yacht, so when I go to sell my boat, my furniture goes with it. I'll keep my fingers crossed that you are able to close the deal on your house.

I know the whole "Smelli" situation really stinks (yes, pun intended). Try not to overthink it like you do everything else. It'll be fine. It WILL work out. Did you try posting something on Facebook? Maybe one of your friends can keep her while you're finding a new place?

I think a healthy dose of change is exactly what you need. I've discovered it's too easy to fall into a false sense of comfort. I think most people are wasting their lives away in that comfortable, convenient place. Besides, starting over is much more interesting and adventurous than the same old thing day in and day out. Challenge yourself, babe. Live outside your comfort zone. I promise you, it's worth it.

I'm personally not a huge fan of vitamins in pill form. Most vitamins are not FDA regulated, and who knows what the hell they actually put in those things. It's best to consume your vitamins by eating the right foods. Try not to take the easy way out with your nutrition.

Love you.

Subject: About my dad
Wednesday, March 27, 2013, at 7:33 PM
To: Wes / From: Mila

Hi Love,

I posted something on Facebook this morning for Nelli. I know I'll find a good home for her! She's a beautiful little tiger. Somebody will snatch her up for that reason alone. Still makes me miserable to think about giving her away. ☹ I feel guilty, like an awful parent who is abandoning her child. She won't understand.

About my dad—I don't usually talk much about his abusive history. You see, he's come a long way over the last fifteen years, and I'm proud of him for the changes he was able to make because most abusive men aren't able to make changes like he has.

When it comes to his interactions with my mom, he remains an easily irritable, mostly negative individual and is draining to be around most of the time, but he has never again laid an abusive hand on her since that fateful day fifteen years ago.

During the formative years of my life, my dad treated my mom pretty terribly. To this day, he still ranks subpar in the "how to treat your spouse" department, but at least he's not physically abusive anymore. He has mellowed a lot over the years. He actually has a lot of good qualities. He treats his children well. He's a good provider and great grandpa. He's also a very considerate neighbor and helpful, giving individual (as long as you are not his wife, that is).

Growing up, I always wanted my parents to divorce. Some days, as awful as it sounds, I actually prayed my dad would die in a car accident. Now before you jump to conclusions about my sinister character, let me explain.

More often than not, my dad made life at home unbearable. He really was two different men. He was an upstanding character in the community while, oftentimes, a terror at home. I think I hated him even more because of that dichotomy.

I knew my mom wasn't ever going to leave him, and as a young child I couldn't see the whole picture. All I could see was the fact that I hated being around him because he scared me and because he hurt my mom, the person I loved more than anyone. So, as human nature goes, I fantasized the most convenient ways to rid him of our lives, which included his death in an accident of some sort. Believe me, I don't like admitting I had these thoughts, because I'm very glad he never died in an accident, but I think it might help you understand how bad things really were … or at least from my point of a view as a timid little girl.

As a defense mechanism, like a meek little mouse, I developed the habit of "hiding" when he would come home. I would close myself up in my bedroom or go to a friend's house to avoid him. I sheltered myself in a lot of ways from his anger and destructive demeanor.

One of my earliest memories goes back to when I was five years old. My dad was fuming about something, I can't remember what. My mom, fearful of his rage, locked herself in the car but couldn't leave because her "kiddos" were still in the house. He hit the car with his fists a few times, but not wanting to seriously damage the car or his hands, he tried to persuade her to get out by threatening to destroy her beloved possessions.

He started bringing things outside and destroying them in front of her, things that brought her joy like her guitar, music books, and family photo albums.

I remember my sister and I sneaked around the house and collected some of my mom's belongings and hid them in our closet. The amount of fear and adrenaline that coursed through my tiny body as his wrath consumed everything in its path was so excessive that I can still distinctly dredge up the sickening feeling as though it happened yesterday. As time passed, arguments like this seemed to become more frequent and increased in severity.

When I was in junior high, my dad's physical abuse hit its culmination point. He was livid about a broken screen door. Sounds ridiculous, right? It had gotten to the point where just about anything would set him off. My mom, legitimately afraid for her life, instructed my sister and me to call 911 if my dad started hurting her. In all of the years of abuse, it was the first time she ever asked one of us to call for help. I knew it was serious, and I was scared to death. I intuitively understood that that night was going to change the course of our lives. I didn't know how; I just knew it would.

That evening, as usual, my mom tried to silently avoid my dad as he ranted at her late into the night. My sister and I sat in our bedroom unwilling to sleep because we knew we had an important job to do.

A nauseating, clawing feeling of fear started ripping at my guts as I heard my dad force my mom to the ground. My mom, in a smothered, muffled voice, called out for my sister, "Reese!"

I screamed in a pathetic, trembling way, "Dad, please stop hurting her! Don't hurt my mom!"

My sister, a much braver person than I, sprang to action. She ran to the office, closed the door, crawled under the desk and called 911. Within minutes, three cop cars surrounded our house. For the first time ever, my dad was hauled off to jail.

That was the last time he ever physically abused her.

My dad, an upstanding character of the farming community and the Catholic church, was horrifically embarrassed the night he was hauled off to jail. He had most of the community convinced he was a pretty stellar dude. And, honestly, for the most part, other than how he treated his wife and sometimes his kids, he was a pretty stellar dude. Had I not been his child, he could've easily fooled me.

Enough about all that, though! It's not something I dwell on. I'm probably a better version of myself for having lived through it.

I'm gonna hit the hay. Work's been kicking my ass lately. Twelve-hour days. Ugh.

Goodnight, babe.

Subject: Self-teaching
Friday, March 29, 2013, at 9:44 PM
To: Mila / From: Wes

Mi amor,

Wow, what an e-mail. Thanks for sharing some of your memories with me. Even though they aren't happy memories, I like learning about you more. Have you ever thought about becoming a writer? I'm sensing some natural talent. I like e-mailing you because you encourage me to be a more thoughtful writer. I don't normally write this well, but I'm making an effort for you.

There's no doubt you had a tumultuous childhood. I knew there was something going on behind the scenes in your home, but I had no idea the extent of it. I'm glad it's not something you dwell on. What's even more awesome is that you believe it impacted you in a GOOD way.

I firmly believe that everything in this world happens for a reason. There are no mistakes in this universe. Think about it. Even the sun is the exact distance from the Earth, to the cunt hair, in order to create and sustain life. Can you believe that? There's a precision to this world, whether you're looking through a telescope or a microscope, which defies intellectual comprehension.

Yes, shitty things happen to good people, and that's difficult to accept as part of the plan. But think of all of the lessons you learned from that fucked-up situation. I bet you can credit your father with being one of your greatest teachers. He probably taught you what kind of spouse you wanted (or didn't want), helped form what kind of person you wanted to become, and provided you compassion for other people struggling with difficult situations.

Just curious, why didn't your mom ever leave him?

On another note, I took my online Algebra II test today. I used my good ol' "creative-thinking" skills and was able to find a website that has a sweet solver program that does everything a long as you type it into the system correctly. I got a 95 percent on the test. ☺

I can't wait to complete my bachelor's degree. What a fuckin' waste of time! I plan to also get my master's degree since I have money available through the GI bill, but let it be known that I have a deep-rooted disdain for college. I haven't learned anything worthwhile yet, and no, it's not because I cheat. The material they teach is a fuckin' joke and not worth my time. I've learned 100 times more attempting something in the real world and failing at it than any class has ever taught me.

I believe in self-teaching. Fortunately, I love to read, so self-teaching comes naturally to me. I heard a quote a long time ago, I can't remember who said it, but I liked it. It goes, "Formal education will make you a living. Self-education will make you a fortune." Sure, some formal education, especially in your youth, is necessary, but I think going to college is a big waste of time and money. Over half of the people that go to college have no idea what they want to do for a lifelong career anyway and realize, when they're thousands of dollars in debt and four years older, that they majored in the wrong field.

I think people should become apprentices and interns after high school and figure out what field they're truly interested in by experiencing it. People would come to learn that most fields don't require a college education to be successful. They require a lot of *experience*.

Gotta get to bed now. Happy early Easter. ☺ I love you.

P.S. I'll be working this weekend and won't be able to communicate with you.

Subject: Cheater, cheater, pumpkin eater
Monday, April 1, 2013, at 7:04 PM
To: Wes / From: Mila

Hey you,

It's funny you should mention it because, yes, I have thought about becoming a novelist. In college, the director of the honors program encouraged me to become a writer. Up until early 2008, I majored in Honors English. However, the financial crisis that started the summer of '07 hadn't improved by second semester, so I decided I needed to consider a more practical career path if I didn't want to be a starving artist the rest of my life. I changed my major to accounting and finished a minor in Honors English instead.

I probably wasn't born to be an accountant. I know I make a good one, but it's certainly not my dream job. It does pay the bills, though!

The question of why my mom never left my dad requires a long and complicated answer that I'm not even sure I could give you. For the sake of brevity, but at the risk of being incomplete, I'll give you a few highlights she has shared with me.

While my dad was a shitty husband, he was a good father for the most part. He was also a great neighbor, an upstanding Catholic, and a good provider. My mom could not stand the thought of breaking up her family. She knew that if she divorced my dad, she would have to share custody with him.

When my dad went to jail, law enforcement mandated a restraining order between my parents for a certain amount of time. Therefore, my dad had to move out of the house for a while. He moved out to the farm and lived with my grandparents. My brothers, young and easily manipulated by him, moved out to the farm with him during that time. It killed my mom. She lost weight faster than a snowman in a skillet. She cried every day, and I believe that is when she decided to try to fix her marriage rather than toss it. She has made a lot of sacrifices over the years to keep her family together. Like I said, my dad never hit her again after he went to jail, but he has also never been a truly loving husband either. She has made more sacrifices than I dare say I would be willing to make.

I wish I shared in your faith and confidence that "everything in this world happens for a reason." It's such an alluring way to think, even if misguided. ☺ I do agree with you that it's indisputable that this world is intelligently designed. I think you would have to be a moron to believe that this wildly intricate creation came together randomly. Yet I'm still wondering if everything in this world happens for a *good* reason. You know what I mean?

I guess it boils down to the old argument of a necessary evil. Must we experience bad in order to fully understand good? From what I know about the human condition, the answer to that question is absolutely yes, we must experience bad if we ever want to understand good. But my follow up question remains the same: If God is capable of all things, why didn't he create humans that are capable of appreciating good without experiencing its opposite? I don't know, sometimes I have a tough time appreciating the beauty in this effed up place we call the world. I've seen a lot of shit. I've said a lot of unanswered prayers. I've witnessed "religious" people behave far more evilly than nonreligious people. I know it's blasphemy to say, but sometimes I feel like if *I* were capable of all things, I would have designed a better, happier world. Then again, these are words spoken from a very jaded mouth.

So, you cheated on your Algebra test, huh? I do NOT condone such behavior, you cheater, cheater, pumpkin eater! I do agree with you that college is generally a crock of crap, though. I love your idea that high school graduates should become apprentices or interns in order to figure out what they want to do with the rest of their lives. And yes, I also believe most careers do not require a college education. I know for a fact that I could be just as successful as an accountant, if not more so, without my four-year degree. Had I not gone to college, I would have four more years of experience under my belt right now, and no textbook in the world could teach me what a few months on the job taught me. In fact, I spent the first month of my job "unlearning" what I learned in college. I wouldn't go so far as to say all of my college education was pointless, but in some ways it certainly set me back in the real world rather than propel me forward. Too bad we have to play by the rules of society, though ...

P.S. For your viewing pleasure, I also attached a naked picture of myself.

P.S.S. Just kidding, no I didn't. Happy April Fools! ☺ Mwahahaha!

Subject: That's just evil
Monday, April 1, 2013, at 10:44 PM
To: Mila / From: Wes

You lil' fuckin' slutterpuss! How dare you tease me with a naked picture?! Now you have to send me one. My brain won't function right until I get it. It's a safety issue, really. Think of all the lives you're endangering if you don't.

On a more serious topic: Believe me when I say I've seen my share of fucked-up things in this world, too. I do believe in a necessary evil, though. I believe experiencing bad is a test of virtue. If you discipline your perspective and mind-set enough, you can draw meaning from senseless bad experiences and make something positive of them—learn from them, grow from them. Think of Viktor Frankl and *Man's Search for Meaning*. Have you read that book? It's one of my favorites.

One thing I've learned, especially after joining the military, is that you can't allow your emotions to control you. We are all emotional. Some people feel certain emotions stronger than others. But you have to learn to discipline your emotions. If you don't discipline them, they will use you.

As far as your job goes, it sounds to me like you don't like being an accountant. Do you think you would like writing better? Another thing I've learned is that our time is too limited to waste it living unhappily. Your work is obviously gonna consume a large portion of your life. So only do work that you believe is fulfilling. Try not to let the Almighty Dollar influence your decisions too much.

Remember our conversation about how life-threatening some of my experiences have been? As you know, I've been forced to come to terms with death. Remembering that I'll be dead soon is the most important tool I've ever encountered to help me make the big choices in life. You'll find that most of your concerns, the roadblocks that prevent you from taking risks, fall away in the face of death. Remembering that you're gonna die is the best way I know to avoid the trap of thinking you have something to lose.

We're going on a short trip this week. I'll e-mail you when I get back. Don't forget to send me that picture!

Love,
Wes

Chapter 10

I hated being left behind. I loathed being the one who always stayed while he traveled God knows where. What I despised the most, though, was when he left for a mission, what he euphemistically called a "trip."

Trip. How I had grown to hate the word. Not being able to talk to him, along with the intuitive understanding that his "trips" were dangerous, drove me batty. The newfound strength and inspiration I found in Wes's presence flew out the window with such ferocity after he deployed that it was like someone opened the hatch of a supersonic aircraft traveling at Mach 5.

Although it's not blatantly evidenced in our exchange of e-mails, I harbored a volatile amount of negative emotions that fermented beneath my superficially resilient exterior. I wished my thoughts and feelings fermented like wine, like his seemed to, only getting better with time, but they didn't. They fermented like vinegar, becoming sour and acidic, burning ulcers inside me. I didn't want Wes to know I was on the verge of erupting like some kind of elementary science fair project mixing vinegar and baking soda.

I wanted to be a good girlfriend and suffer his absence without complaint. I pretended the best I could at being positive, but the effort drained me. I knew I was backsliding from the little progress I made while able to lean on the crutch of his company. But now that he was gone, a feral restlessness collapsed upon me, as though his deployment cut away the last fiber that attached me to rationality.

After he deployed, I let go of what little emotional control I possessed, allowing the waves of my feelings to sweep me out into an ocean of bleakness. I cried more, yelled more, smoked a lot more pot, and lashed out at God in the privacy of my own home when the world threatened to overpower me.

I told myself that until I sold my house there was no way I could consider changing my job yet again, and my job was taking over every last bit of energy reserve I had in store. I worked as many hours at my new job as I had at my old. *So much for escaping the rat race.* Between work and my time consuming personal affairs, in terms of selling my house, relocating my beloved Nelli, and figuring out where I was headed with my future, I hardly kept my head above water.

I was spread so thin it physically manifested in my increasingly thinning physique. I wouldn't go so far as to describe myself as deathly thin, but I was not normal thin, either. My family started murmuring concerns about my ghoulish gauntness, which I conveniently ignored. Dark crescent moons took shape under my eyes and my first wrinkle, a cavernous line between my eyebrows resulting from furrowing my face in stress, eroded its unappealing path at the young age of 26.

Wes shared a lot of great advice in his e-mails, but I wasn't ready to hear what he had to say. His advice annoyed me. It pointed out all of my flaws at a time I felt my hands were tied, and I secretly blamed him for making my life more complicated than it needed to be. Instead of taking his and my family's advice to heart, I lived my life with my fingers in my ears, as though the truth would not exist if I never heard the words spoken aloud.

Don't get me wrong, I wanted to change my life, knew that I needed to change it, but the struggle was real. Wes was gone. I was alone. And my kneecaps buckled under the pressure of it all. Unhappiness fatigued me like a disease. I couldn't escape the feeling of anxiety. It was like a dull current surging through me, and it flowed into everything I did.

I allowed myself to believe I might find happiness once I sold my house. Or perhaps after I found a loving home for Nelli. Or maybe I would find it after I got a new job. I thought of happiness like the many arrowhead-hunting quests I undertook with my dad as a kid. If I just kept my head down and plugged along long enough, happiness might appear before me like a rare stone hiding in the earth. I just needed to grit my teeth, keep moving forward, and cross my fingers for a little luck.

My sister-in-law, Lucy, helped me find a suitable home for my sweet puppy and just in time, too. I relocated her one week prior to closing on the sale of my house. One of Lucy's acquaintances was looking to adopt a dog. He lived adjacent to a large city park and wanted an active dog like Nelli. I wasn't sure about the match since Nelli typically feared men, however, I felt like I didn't have much choice in the matter. Time was running short. Luckily, he was a small, gentle, soft-spoken man Nelli seemed to interact with okay. Right off the bat, he loved her gorgeous brindle coloring, athletic build, and affectionate personality. He promised he'd take great care of her. Sadly, I had to let her go.

I sobbed every day when I got home from work for an entire week after he took her. I would close the door behind me and lean up against it, slowly slipping to the floor in a puddle of tears. My Nelli-Belly was not there to greet me with her nasty, slobbery kisses and wagging tail, hazardously whipping my thighs. Although I knew it was the right decision to provide her a permanent home that could give her the amount of attention she deserved, I missed her terribly, and I worried she missed me, too. I felt like a total failure as a dog owner.

Even though I knew it was a blessing I was able to provide her a good home, that did not stop me from thinking about how God had, yet again, taken from me something that I loved.

I closed on the sale of my house the second week of April. I didn't make a dime, but I also didn't lose much money either. I gave away most of my belongings. I downsized from a four-bedroom house to a single bedroom in my parents' basement. Downsizing felt cleansing, but I couldn't shake the feeling that I was moving in reverse. Living with my parents, in some ways, was like being in high school again, only worse, because this time I had to find a place to hide all of my new bad habits, namely my skunky pot.

From my parents' house, I lived an hour and twenty minutes away from work if traffic was good, and traffic was never good. I left my parents' house around five in the morning and did not return until late in the evening, sometimes not until after ten o'clock. My parents' frequently commented on my imbalanced lifestyle saying I worked too much and I didn't eat or sleep enough. I kept telling them (and myself) the situation was only temporary.

Not long after I closed on my house and moved into my parents' basement, my mom and I joined Birdie for lunch at WeatherBee Ranch. Being like-minded individuals, the three of us chatted for hours before anybody realized how much time had passed. The visit was like aloe to my blistered soul. Both Birdie and my mom emitted an infectious positive energy. Also, being near Birdie and at WeatherBee Ranch somehow made me feel closer to Wes, which was important because I felt further from him with each passing day.

I could tell Birdie was worried about me. It didn't take a brain surgeon to see I was in bad shape. She started e-mailing me and asking to get together with me regularly after that. It marked the beginning of a close relationship that played a key role in my future.

After only three short weeks of living with my parents, Ruger ran away. Moving away from his home and his best friend, Señor Don Gato, traumatized my poor Roogy-Poogy. Not to mention my parents owned a small dog that lived in the house, and the two of them did not hit it off. He wasn't a happy camper, but I didn't expect him to run away from me. I'll never know what became of my darling, mischievous cat.

My already broken heart could hardly take losing another loved one. It seemed like my world was decomposing. Losing first Wes, then Nelli, and now Ruger, each presented a difficult undertaking individually, but combined they became an anguish almost unbearable. I tried to turn to Wes for sympathy but found little. By this time, Wes had programmed his phone so we could text as long as he had Wi-Fi.

FRIDAY, MAY 10, 2013

```
Mila:  hey babe. roogy ran away. ☹
Wes:   i'm sorry. ☹ u sure?
Wes:   maybe he's just exploring?
Wes:   making new friends?
Mila:  he's been gone for a whole week now
Mila:  he's been MIA before but never for this
       long …
Wes:   he might still show up
Wes:   it'll be fine love
Mila:  is that all u ever say?!
Wes:   haha. i guess... it really will be fine
       mila. you'll see
Wes:   luv u ☺
Mila:  i love u too
```

Looking back, texting those words, "I love u," left a thin film of sadness when it should have done the exact opposite. In the face of his absence, words that always seemed so immense felt small now. What was love when put up against deployment after having known each other for really no time at all? Distance and time can rub the familiarly right off someone, even if you've known them your whole life.

Our e-mails and texts seemed intimate enough, but they didn't hold a candle to what it was like between us when we were physically together. At this point, my mouth could no longer remember the taste of his tongue. My ears could no longer remember the sound of his voice. By this time, the touch of his hand was nothing but a ghostly imprint. Certain details of my memories were slipping away like sand in an hourglass, while other memories seemed to crystallize. It's hard to explain.

Losing a loved one does funny things to your memories. In my case, worry conspired with fear and wrinkled the edges of them. I could no longer tease forth the exact memories. I wondered if, rationally, much of what I remembered of him was romanticized by the tragedy of time, any adverse qualities swallowed up by my ache for him. I thought maybe my mind had somehow warped my recollections—mysteriously smoothing them with the passage of time, shedding all of their intricacies like the scales of a snake's skin and making them seem more perfect than they really were. Time can do that. It has an eerie way of bleaching away the sense of things until all that remains is bone-white memories blanched of their complexities.

My mind played tricks on me, and what began as a hint of an apparition of uneasiness had grown to a conscious voice. Was it real? Or did the trauma of our limited time release some kind of dopamine that otherwise wouldn't have been present if the situation were more typical? I mean, I knew he was great, but was he all I was making him out to be? And if he were, could I ever be enough for a man like him? How long would it take before he was bored with me? He had never been with the same woman for much more than a month, so I imagined it wouldn't take long before boredom settled in like a Trojan horse, misrepresenting itself as something normal and routine before it stealthily infected his thoughts with the malicious virus of ennui.

And these were the types of queries that rose like a specter in the shadows of too much rumination (most likely brought on by too much medical-grade marijuana). They dragged their fangs through my brain, gnawed at me until my mind became mush with insecurities.

Chapter 11

Subject: Monday morning smile
Monday, May 20, 2013, at 4:02 AM
To: Mila / From: Wes

Good morning, Beautiful.

I just wanted to give you a smile for your Monday morning, and let you know that I miss you. I was up super early this morning, considering I slept most of yesterday.

I'm thinking Hank and I are gonna do some fishing today off the rocks outside of our apartment. Hank caught four pretty good-sized barracudas the other night. I've been anxious to reel in a few myself.

I'm also gonna drum up the motivation to run the stairs behind our apartment. We're located at the bottom of a 1,500-foot hill that used to be home to a huge gun battery and bunker in the WW2–Korea era. There are steps going straight up the bunker. It's a real dick dragger. I can barely make it to the top without stopping.

What are you up to today? You know, come to think of it, I don't know much at all about your job. Tell me more about what you do. I hope you don't end up working another 12-hour day!

Love you.

Subject: Thanks for the smile
Monday, May 20, 2013, at 8:14 PM
To: Wes / From: Mila

Babe,

Thanks for the Monday morning smile. ☺ I'm actually still at work right now. I'm expecting long days until we hammer out the new terms of the insurance policy for the fiscal year starting July 1.

You really want to know more about my job? LOL… Okay, I'll do my best to keep it simple, but prepare yourself for extreme boredom!

I manage the financial responsibilities for two insurance companies domiciled in Hawaii. One insurance company is a risk retention group (RRG) and the other company reinsurances the RRG and is called a sister pure captive.

Right now, I'm determining the best way to update the accounting terms in all of the new policy agreements to achieve the desired profitability goals outlined by the companies' directors and officers as well as all of the state regulators.

For an RRG, profitability is an important consideration since insurance regulators in all of the states the company writes policies (twelve in this case) have certain benchmarks of solvency that must be met. To make things more complicated, construction defect liability, unlike let's say car insurance, is a more volatile industry, which presents many challenges in forecasting the amount of premiums necessary to cover future losses. For these companies, the losses for one policy could extend for up to ten years. In fact, this particular industry is so unpredictable that many insurers have stopped writing this line of business, making it difficult for builders and subcontractors to find adequate coverage.

Presently, I'm determining the best premium split between the two companies. To do this, I create forecasts that look at various scenarios by changing certain key assumptions. I use actuarial analyses to help project losses and historical data to help project premiums based on the number of homes closed estimated by each home-building division.

There are several regulated factors I must take into consideration like the risk-based capital ratio, which is far too complicated to try to explain. At any rate, I prepare a handful of forecasted scenarios along with a few other analyses to present to the officers and board of directors, along with my personal recommendations. They will then discuss and vote on a final percent split. This and several other terms for renewal are ultimately translated into a written agreement that is signed by an authorized representative of each company.

Capeesh? ☺

Anyway, I'm gonna finish up this spreadsheet if my eyelids will hold out. Fishing for barracuda sounds like a lot more fun ... I hope you still have all of your fingers. ☺

Love you more,

Milena Rudenko, CPA
Statutory Accounting Department
R.K.D. Holdings, Inc.
8810 S. Belleview Dr. #600 | Denver, CO 80237
Direct Phone: 751.555.1005 / Ext: 991005 |
milena.rudenko@rkd.com

Subject: Biting triggerfish

Tuesday, May 21, 2013, at 9:22 AM
To: Mila / From: Wes

Mi amor,

I'm only a little sorry I asked. ☺ I can't even pretend to understand what you do. You're such a geek! Remind me to give you a wedgie when I get home.

I have to admit, it's kinda sexy when you talk like that, though, all genius-like. Your brain, after all, is one of the main reasons I fell in love with you. I love me some hot nerd! Oh, that reminds me, you still need to send me that naked picture! Don't make me beg.

I wish you could see how beautiful the water is here and how abundant the sea life. One of my all-time favorite hobbies is spearfishing. I can't wait to take you someday. I think you'd love it. Shooting a fish is much more exciting than hooking one! Not only is it more exciting, but it's also more efficient as you get to choose which fish you murk instead of crossing your fingers and hoping for a good one. Hank and I decided to go spearfishing yesterday instead.

We've gone a few times since we got settled in. Each time we go, we end up getting a bunch of great fish. Our freezer has been full of amazing, fresh seafood for weeks now. We plan to feed ourselves this way for the rest of the trip. Cheap on the pocket and entertaining in the process.

Our favorite fish to hunt is triggerfish. Are you familiar? They're rather thinly shaped but can grow to the size of a large serving platter. The meat is white with a steak-like texture. You mentioned you tried swordfish while you were in Portugal, right? Triggerfish is similar in taste and texture. It makes some of the best ceviche I've ever had!

They're so tasty mostly because they feed on some of the most delicious things in the ocean such as clams and oysters. One can imagine, though, the teeth that are necessary in order to get to these hard-shelled treats. Triggerfish teeth are a mix between a great white's pointy teeth and protruding goat's teeth. Fuckin' goofy lookin' bastards.

Our common practice is to spear them and then place them into a large mesh bag that hangs from our hips as we continue to fish. Today I was happily swimming along with a couple of triggerfish in my mesh bag when I felt a crushing and tearing sensation in my leg. As I kicked around, I noticed a quarter-sized hole in my leg where a recently speared, but very much alive, triggerfish had taken a bite out of me. Needless to say, I'll enjoy eating *that* fish above all the rest!

We're leaving for another trip today. I won't be able to contact you for about a week.

Love and miss you so much!

TUESDAY, MAY 21, 2013

Mila: hey babe just got ur email

Mila: i'm totally jealous of ur spearfishing adventures

Mila: minus the grumpy guy that bit u of course ☺

Wes: can u believe that asshole?!

Wes: oh well he'll be extra tasty ☺

Mila: lol at least u still have all of ur fingers

Mila: when r u leaving for ur "trip"

Wes: in the next couple hours

Wes: packing dead hooker bags now

Mila: dead hooker bags?

Wes: lol that's what we call em

Mila: why?

Wes: cuz u could fit a dead hooker in one

Mila: oh. lol. classy

Wes: right? i didn't come up with the name lol

Mila: haha ok be safe love u

Wes: luv u more!

Mila: [image attached]

Wes: oh. my. god. ☺

Wes: ur so fuckin sexy. thanks for not making me beg haha

```
Wes:   saving it to my photo vault now
Wes:   i can't wait to rape the shit out of u
Mila:  the feeling is mutual ☺
```

WEDNESDAY, MAY 29, 2013

```
Wes:   hey u. just got back
Mila:  nice. i'm glad u made it back safely ☺
Mila:  missed u ♥
Wes:   miss u always babe ♥ ♥ ♥!!
Wes:   we're gonna go fishing to unwind a bit.
       i'll email you tonight
Wes:   p.s. i've looked at that pic like 100
       times
Mila:  ☺
```

Subject: Peacock bass
Wednesday, May 29, 2013, at 8:52 PM
To: Mila / From: Wes

Mi amor,

We went out on the lake today for some fishing. We traveled about an hour outside the city. We paid a local named Cesar who is about five' two", 250 pounds to take us on his 10-foot jon boat. He drove us around and fished with us all morning while sitting Indian style somehow.

Peacock bass, I guess, are a big thing for anglers in this area, but they just look like bass to me. They're fun to catch, though, and even better to eat. The best way to catch them is simply a small hook with a minnow and light weights on the line. We ended up catching about a dozen of these things. When we got back to the dock, Cesar's kids ran out and filleted them all in about two minutes.

Cesar's wife cooked them up for us and, boy, were they delicious! There must be something about catching your own dinner that makes it yummier.

The boss man caught the biggest one today at about four pounds. I attached two pictures of me with my biggest catches of the day, coming in at second and third place.

Don't be bamboozled, though ... my real "peacock" always comes in first. ☺

Love,
Wes

Subject: You're killin' me, Smalls
Wednesday, May 29, 2013, at 10:44 PM
To: Wes / From: Mila

Hey babe,

Sounds like another incredible fishing adventure. Makes me wonder what the hell I'm doing with my life. Here I am punching numbers into a computer all day until my eyes blur with exhaustion, while there you are living a life more akin to a beachy vacation. I don't know why you would ever want to come home.

I'm gonna hit the hay. I can't stand to look at a computer screen for one more second today.

P.S. I love your pictures. They make me miss you even more, as if that's possible. You look phenomenal—so happy, healthy, tanned, and handsome. Can't wait to get a taste of your trophy peacock, if you know what I mean. ☺

Chapter 12

I remember being pestered by a sense of dread later that week when I hadn't heard back from Wes. I kept checking my texts and e-mails, literally more than a hundred times a day. Since he had deployed, he'd always been very good about telling me when I wouldn't be able to get in touch with him, so, even though I didn't like it, at least I knew when he wouldn't be around.

This time he didn't say anything like that, though. It'd been three days since I last heard from him and, unless he was on a mission, that never happened. If he was around, I heard from him every single day without exception. At a very minimum, I received a little "good morning" or "goodnight" text but generally received many more than that.

I tried to keep my anxiety in check, but worry started to overtake my every thought. I considered all the worst things that might've happened to him. Awful thoughts. I attempted to take such terrible thoughts and stick them as far back into my mental filing cabinet as they would go, under the drawer labeled Unthinkable. But they fought their way back to the forefront of my mind, especially at night when darkness and weariness weakened my self-control and made me more susceptible to the creep of ghastly things.

These thoughts, they strangled all other thoughts. They choked me like a giant hand of foreboding. With every textless minute that passed, the ominous presentiment grew stronger. I felt certain that this unshakable feeling was a premonition that something terrible was going to happen or maybe already had happened to him. Like somehow I possessed an internal third eye that could see around the curve of time and this feeling wasn't just a feeling, it was a fatal message from my intuition—a message I could do nothing about. And the result of all of this worrying without being able to do anything about it, screwed something in me tighter and tighter.

I, of course, tried to reach out to him countless times, but my phone remained stubbornly, insolently blank. I could tell my texts were successfully sending, too, because I didn't receive failure notices, which meant his phone was connected to Wi-Fi. *Where the hell are you? Please write back.*

After a week of worry, I texted Birdie a panicky message. She attempted to put my mind at ease and invited me over for some coffee. She told me it wasn't unusual for Wes to fall off the grid periodically. "It's the nature of the beast we call the military," she said, giving me a sympathetic smile. I nodded my head in agreement but thought to myself: *Maybe it isn't unusual for him to fall off the grid with you, his parent. I mean, he's a grown-ass man ... but it's very unusual for him to fall of the grid with me, his "amor."*

No matter what, I couldn't make the bad feeling go away. Parts of me were separating, I could physically feel it. The fabric of my sanity spooled apart and knotted on the ground before me.

All the while, other parts of me wound ever tighter. After not hearing from him for nearly two weeks, I was strung so tight I felt like an over-tuned violin. Even the smallest tremor, unnoticeable to the average person, set me humming. And then it finally happened.

I snapped.

Subject: I can't do this
Friday, June 14, 2013, at 11:55 PM
To: Wes / From: Mila

Wes,

At this point, I haven't heard from you in over two weeks. If you're reading this e-mail, you, no doubt, already know that, though, as I'm sure you just finished reading the countless texts I sent you over the course of your absence.

I'm literally worried sick about you. I'm at the point where I can't eat or sleep. Whenever I try to lie still, my mind whirrs to life like an overwound toy. My brain is both wired and weary, which is a strange contradiction of states.

I'm absolutely miserable, Wes. I feel so much misery that I can't even feel misery anymore. I know that seems impossible, but it's like my survival mechanism stepped in and said "enough is enough." Yesterday I felt everything at once, but today I feel nothing at all. Zilch. Zippo. Nada. And quite frankly, I don't know which one is worse, drowning beneath a sea of suffering or dying from the thirst of apathy.

But you probably don't know anything about that, do you? You've probably never worried about anyone that way. You probably always have control of your thoughts and emotions. In fact, you're probably fishing right now, shootin' the breeze with your co-swickles while enjoying a cold brewsky. You're probably not wondering at all what I'm doing because, naturally, you already know what I'm doing. The same fucking shit I do every day—counting somebody else's beans.

Does it make me a bad person that knowing you're enjoying yourself and making the most of this deployment, rather than being miserable and lonely like me, actually makes me angry and feel less loved? Every time I hear about one of your fucking fishing or diving adventures the pit of my stomach churns with envy and gloom. I guess my fear is that you'll have so much fun on this deployment you'll have no reason to ever stop deploying, in which case I should just give up now because I don't want to do this. I *can't* do this.

You know, it was hard enough for me to trust you, especially with you being a proudly self-professed male whore who fucks anything that stands still long enough. Yes, the same little strumpet who volunteered for a deployment in South America and who, not so coincidentally, finds South American women the most attractive of all women he has so unbiasedly humped over the years. But I got over that. That was hard enough. But now I'm also supposed to trust a man who disappears with no warning? Who has no accountability to me whatsoever?

Truthfully, I'm mad as fuck. I know it's unreasonable, but I can't help it. It's the way I feel, and the harder I try to bury it, the more it boils in my belly brewing ulcers of acrimony. I'm mad at everything and everyone.

I'm mad at you, Wesley. I'm mad at you for making me fall in love with you, casting your goddamn spell over me with your irresistible charm. I'm mad at you for renewing your contract when you didn't have to and *choosing* to leave me behind. And now that you're gone, I'm mad at you for not feeling miserable the way I do. I'm mad at you for obviously not caring for me as much as I do for you.

I'm mad at my employer. I'm mad that I constantly feel undervalued and overworked. That I'm run ragged even though I'm an honest, hardworking employee who deserves a life outside of the office.

I'm mad at God. I'm mad at Him for taking away the things I love, mercilessly. I'm mad at Him for implanting good and moral desires in my heart that go unfulfilled despite my best efforts. I'm mad at Him for playing me for the fool I am time and time again.

But mostly, I'm mad at me. I'm mad that I possess the intelligence and aptitude to do anything in this world, and, yet, I find myself stuck in these all-consuming jobs I dread. I'm mad at me for continuing down this unhealthy path, knowingly and willingly, when I know I'm so much better than that. I'm mad at me for allowing myself to fall in love with someone I barely know, someone I knew would leave me and ultimately put me in this very maddening situation.

I can't stand how dark and ugly my thoughts are, Wesley, how bottomless my grief and anger. Something *has* to change.

With your disappearance entered a million little doubts. And those doubts shaped an awareness. An awareness that has poked at me with the persistence of a petulant child. An awareness that reminded me that there are lots of potential problems with this relationship, and the more I think about it, the more convinced I am that I made a terrible mistake agreeing to it. I ignored my practicality for my passion, and it backfired, like it tends to do. I should've known better, but love, life ... these things are hard to govern.

The bottom line, Wes—I can't do this anymore. I love you, but I fucking <u>hate</u> this.

My anger reservoir contained a greater capacity than I'd imagined, and that e-mail, I thought, was generous in not sharing the total volume of it. I reread that e-mail a million times before I sent it. I groped at the words. My tongue fondled every sentence until I could recite them by heart. My words felt small and sharp and mean, like a box of tacks, but I didn't care. I wanted them to be mean. I wanted them to poke and cut and stick him. I wanted him to hurt like I hurt. He deserved to feel at least one ounce of the ton of pain inflicted on me. And I could've been so much meaner.

I didn't consciously realize I was debating whether or not to send the e-mail. I never intended on not sending it. But apparently there was some sort of inner debate happening since I couldn't bring myself to hit the send button, at least not right away.

Eventually, I mustered the audacity to do it, and I recall with remarkable clarity that something in my soul shut its scaly eyes right as I pressed the button. Then almost from nowhere, the horror rose within me like bile. I said what I set out to say, but I didn't feel what I set out to feel. *What did I just do?*

I didn't *really* want to break up with him. I wanted nothing more than to be with him, to be able to talk to him. Did I honestly believe that breaking up with him would solve the problem of not being able to talk to him? Did I think that breaking up with him would make me miss him less? Make me less miserable? *What the hell did I just do?*

I wanted to snatch the words back out of cyber-air, like fireflies, but they'd already crawled their way into Wes's computer and illuminated my craziness.

Even though I had it memorized, I reread the e-mail incessantly. Part of me hoped that, somehow, as if by some sort of miracle, the words would transmute. That over the past several days of rereading it, the words would've disbanded into tiny particles that I could just blow away like dust, leaving nothing but a harmless blank page. But when I gave my screen a mighty huff and a puff like a fairy-tale wolf, nothing happened. The screen didn't so much as politely quiver. The letters, like tacks, clung in place.

Subject: I'm so sorry
Monday, June 17, 2013, at 11:07 PM
To: Mila / From: Wes

Mila,

First off, let me say how sorry I am for not telling you I'd be gone for a couple of weeks. We left for a trip unexpectedly. I didn't even have time to grab my toothbrush, let alone send out a text. I should've warned you about the possibility of vanishing without notice. I'm sorry that you worried about me. I wanted to contact you, but I honestly had no way of doing so. I'm really sorry.

Have I ever mentioned to you that dealing with the DoD is like swimming in a circular pool of jelly? We usually end up right where we started and move at the speed of molasses. I'm sorry you were hurt unnecessarily.

Coming "home" to all of your concerned texts and ultimately your breakup e-mail was the last way I wanted to end a real shit storm of a trip. To say that I'm disappointed would be the understatement of the century. I don't want you to break up with me, Mila. But I also won't ask you to wait for me. I can only hope you find it in your heart to do so.

Love,

Wes

I shut my eyes for a moment, battling to compose myself before I continued absorbing his response. Tears fought to the surface, suspended momentarily by surface tension, and then spilled over, streaming hot down my cheeks.

What a relief. *What a huge fucking relief.* Relief flooded my system like morphine. I was relieved, first and foremost, that I finally knew he was alive and okay. Secondly, that I had been given another chance. He didn't want to break up. Even after my belligerent e-mail, he didn't want to break up. I thought, *maybe I can still fix this.*

For the first time in a long time, I looked skyward and shared a moment of gratitude with God. "Thank you," I audibly whispered. "Thank you, *thank you.*"

MONDAY, JUNE 17, 2013

Mila: hey i just read ur email

Mila: i'm so sorry for losing it ☹

Mila: i'm really glad ur okay

Wes: it's ok. i understand. that was stress-ful for u

Wes: though u did kinda blow ur fuckin nuts off haha

Wes: i'm sorry for putting u thru that

Mila: i don't want to break up. i'm such a
      jackass
Wes: u ok babe? seems like there's more go-
      ing on here than just u being worried
      about me
Mila: idk i'm a mess
Wes: what's the deal?
Mila: i'm caught in a bubble of negativity
      and i can't seem to pop it
Wes: what's bringing u down?
Mila: a lot of stuff. mainly work and u being
      gone
Wes: what's going on at work?
Mila: nothing really. i just work too much
Mila: i'm gone at least 12 hours a day with
      travel. often times more
Wes: ok. that's easy. find a new job ☺
Mila: lol yeah i'm working on a solution
Wes: good
Wes: why r u still hung up on me being gone?
Wes: it's only temporary
Mila: i know
Mila: it's like a mind virus or something
Mila: i'm stuck in a world that's more a pro-
      jection of my fears than reality
Wes: what do u fear?
Mila: a bunch of stuff that doesn't really
      exist
Mila: or at least not yet

```
Wes:   like?
Mila:  like allowing myself to be truly vul-
       nerable with u and getting hurt somehow
Mila:  u might die while ur doing whatever it
       is ur doing
Mila:  u might cheat on me because u could
       very easily and i would never know
Mila:  u might never stick around and i might
       always be longing for more
Mila:  i dunno wes. a bunch of stuff i have no
       real control over i guess
Wes:   exactly. u have no control over those
       things
Mila:  the only control i have is to distance
       myself from it all before i get in too
       deep … hence the breakup
Wes:   well then u need to make a choice
Wes:   do u wanna live in the present moment
       and deal with whatever comes when it
       comes or do u wanna live in fear of a
       future u have little control over?
Mila:  the present moment
Wes:   then come back to reality babe
Mila:  i'm trying
Mila:  can i start over?
Wes:   yes
Mila:  good. hope i didn't do too much damage
       here
```

```
Wes:   it'll be fine
Mila:  lol. yes of course "it'll be fine" … it
       always is according to u
Wes:   yes and i'm usually right ☺
Mila:  i wouldn't go that far
Wes:   luv u
Mila:  love u too ☺
```

Chapter 13

Holy fuckballs ... that was a close call. I can't believe I did that! Almost threw it all away like that! I'm so grateful he's still in my life. Jesus, what's wrong with me?

Tears burned my eyes, but I refused to wipe them away. My burning tears served a purgative purpose. They acted as telescopes, aiding me to see more clearly. Our near breakup helped me see things in myself I'd been turning a blind eye to. It was as if my vision suddenly renewed, my eyes abruptly washed clean of the dark lens distorting my view.

But now that my eyes were seeing more clearly, I desperately didn't want to see through them. They unveiled to me my shortcomings, how I had invited fear, anger, envy, and other evil emotions to manipulate my perception and influence my behaviors.

The reality of the choices I'd made suddenly seemed to weigh heavily on my shoulders like a giant, guilty stone. I felt crushed beneath an invisible anvil of truth. I thought I was better than that, smarter than that. I judged my place in the world from a superior position, but now I could see that even with all of my intellectual introspection, I was not immune to deceiving myself.

I covered my eyes with my hands as if to summon new deceits to mask the gaping emptiness left by my freshly acquired insight. I toyed with conjuring new delusions that might offer refuge from the onslaught of embarrassment and staggering disappointment that dragged me down, drowning me in a dark well of foul feelings.

But once you see, you can't un-see. And, as the saying goes: before the truth sets you free, it's apt to make you miserable.

I dropped my hands from my eyes, and they instinctively clasped over my aching heart. I sat there digesting my current condition, trying not to hate everything about myself. Vibrations of self-pity and self-loathing sang a sad, low song in my inner ears. The tapestry of my soul unraveled and ripped apart as I tried to comprehend what the fuck was wrong with me.

I possessed so much unharnessed potential. *I am a smart, talented person ... How the hell did I get to this place?* A place of sadness and dissatisfaction. A place where I used drugs to sleepwalk my way through life. A place where I justified my bad decisions solely because I felt I had the right to, due to a lifetime of making too many of the "right" decisions without getting the happiness I deserved. A place I didn't want others to see because of its ugliness. An uninviting, isolating place. I hated that I exposed even a glimpse of this place to Wes.

I sat there pondering the multitude of decisions that directed me down the path to this place. There wasn't one significant, life-altering event that propelled me in this direction. There was no lightning bolt that zapped me down this course. Rather it came as a slow crystallization of my responses to life's challenges— the unbalancing of priorities as a result of a growing ego, the daily submission to anxiety and negativity, the loss of trust that everything works out for the best if you give your best ... the list goes on and on. It was a lifetime of choices that individually did not seem to matter much, but cumulatively formed a hard, murky crystal of undesirable qualities.

Before opening my eyes to this realization, from my prior point of view, I would've said that "life" just happened. That's how I got to this place. Big and little losses wrapped inside the everyday. But from my new perspective, I could now see that it was death, not life, that drove me here. It was a small, hardly perceptible death here and there of the elemental truths tucked deep inside my soul. It was un-love, un-faith, un-truth, un-hope, an un-reality I was not designed or destined for. It was death. It was the slow dimming of my inner light.

I became like the proverbial frog in slow boiling water. As the allegory goes, if you drop a frog in a pot of water that is already boiling, it'll jump out, but if you put a frog in cool water and slowly bring it to a boil, it'll cook. And I was, without a doubt, cooking.

My personal awareness of my problem with ... well, I'll just call it negativity ... came about slothfully mostly because I learned early in life how to craft excellent justifications and then refine them, if necessary, to explain my ever-deteriorating life as something outside of my own responsibility. But finally, after breaking up with Wes, I experienced an epiphany of sorts that helped me recognize such unkind consequences as a direct spinoff of my own choices. I guess you could say the accountant finally became accountable.

This was certainly depressing at first. I could no longer pass the buck. But keeping the blame, rather than shifting it, hurt horribly. I believe it was the misery of this revelation that actually pushed me to make a new choice.

That's the thing about misery. Once you're in it up to your eyeballs, you'll do just about anything to find a way out. Sometimes the way out is healthy, where you grow and change and adapt. Other times it's unhealthy, where you medicate and distract yourself from the truths life is trying to teach you. I knew all too well what the latter led to. So now, I understood I had to make a different choice. I finally felt ready to put forth the required effort to turn things around rather than continue marauding down a deadly path of un-fulfillment.

But that was just one choice of an immeasurable number of choices to come. My entire lifestyle had to be rehabilitated in order to outwit and triumph over negativity in all choices (or at least the vast majority of them), even the smallest, seemingly pointless ones.

So where do I start? That's what I asked myself, feeling almost immediately overwhelmed. I sat silently, said a prayer of contrition and another for guidance. Then, as if by magic, the answer rose from within. My very quiet, recently oppressed, inner voice whispered faintly. *Start small. First, do what is necessary. Once you've mastered that, graduate to what's possible. Keep excelling. Keep improving. Take one day at a time. One hour. One minute. Stick with it. Whatever you do, don't give up.*

And I did just that.

First, I committed to taking daily walks with my mom. Simply getting out and breathing fresh air was a hugely transformative step. Sharing conversation with my lifelong confidante renewed my strength.

Next, I picked up a philosophical book focused on positivity. Systematically I made all sorts of small changes. Over the course of the next few months I stopped drinking insane quantities of Mountain Dew. I made healthier choices when it came to food consumption. I smoked a lot less pot. I set aside time for meditation. I particularly found peace in meditating/praying while sitting in my parents' hot tub after dark and alone while peering into the starry night sky. I endeavored to build new, meaningful friendships with people who inspired me to be better. I read more books. Lots and lots of positive and spiritual books. I witnessed the sentences of those books hoist me up and carry me somewhere else, to a new and better place.

Gradually, in an incremental capacity, I changed. I improved. I excelled. At first, the process felt awkward and tremendously challenging. Bad habits can't just be flicked out the window like a pesky insect. They have to be coaxed down the stairs one step at a time like a big, stubborn bull.

In the beginning, it felt as though I were acting, pretending to be a more positive, healthier person when actually a negative, unhealthy version of me loitered just beneath the surface, dying to pull me back under, waiting for any small excuse to drag me backward. Eventually, though, as with all things that are consistently practiced, it got easier.

And I finally felt *good*.

Subject: Happy Birthday!
Monday, July 1, 2013, at 5:15 PM
To: Wes / From: Mila

Hey babe,

HAPPY BIRTHDAY! I know I already texted you that, but since I can't tell you in person, I guess I'll tell you twice. 😊

Today is a rare slow day at work, so I thought how better to pass the time than to write you a birthday card.

First of all, you might be interested to know what attracted me to you on our first date. Many of the bullet points below I already told you or you've probably figured out by now, but it can't hurt to reiterate them.

* We shared easy conversation.
* You seemed a little nervous at first, which I thought was endearing ... but you were also surprisingly confident.
* Physically, I'm certain I've NEVER been more attracted to or had stronger chemistry with any other person I've ever met (even the thought of our first kiss gives me butterflies to this day!!).
* I was impressed by your view on discipline and dedication.
* I was captivated by your well-balanced, seemingly consistent, positive approach to life.

* I liked the way you touched me—assured and commanding, yet unpredictably gentle.
* I felt safe with you.
* You inspired me, without really meaning to, to be a better person.

The real purpose of this e-mail, though, is to get something off of my chest. Generally speaking, I'm a pretty open person with the people I trust, though it's a challenge communicating with people when I'm not face-to-face with them. I rely a lot on reading people's expressions, I guess. There's something I've been wanting to tell you, but haven't found the right time or the courage to bring it up.

Overall, I feel like it's arguable that you've gotten an unfavorable snapshot of my personality. Since before I started talking to you on a regular basis, I was going through a lot of changes in a very small window of time. I changed just about everything I'd known consistently over the past four years. I went through a very difficult long-distance breakup. I put my house on the market. I started a new job. I fell in love with a man that put me right back into a situation I swore I'd never be in again. I moved. I lost both of my pets. And I'm currently considering finding yet another new job and buying yet another house (just to name a few things!). I've been actively resisting these changes and have pitied myself quite dramatically along the way.

Typically, I would say I'm a fairly mellow, level-headed person. However, lately that has not been the case. I can't even pinpoint when the roller-coaster ride started, but it has certainly been in full swing since you've known me. I feel genuinely guilty for subjecting you to that, and I want to take this opportunity to apologize to you. I'm also embarrassed you witnessed me behave in a way I'm not very proud of, because I really adore you and feel like I've given you a bad impression of my character. The worst part is that I've hidden much of my craziness from you, so I've actually been a lot shittier than you even know.

Breaking up with you catalyzed a much-needed awakening. I've been swimming in a lot of self-inflicted conflict lately, and coming very close to losing you (due to no fault but my own), helped me realize some ugly truths I've been deliberately ignoring for years.

Anyway, I've committed to practicing a least one small habit of self-improvement daily. I can sit here and describe to you some of the progress I've made, but it's always better to show and not tell. I hope you begin to see changes in me, as I'm absolutely devoted to improving my state of being. I hope to be a much healthier, lovelier version of myself by the time we reunite in October.

With love,

Milena Rudenko, CPA
Statutory Accounting Department

R.K.D. Holdings, Inc.
8810 S. Belleview Dr. #600 | Denver, CO 80237
Direct Phone: 751.555.1005 / Ext: 991005 |
milena.rudenko@rkd.com

Subject: You are beautiful to me
Monday, July 1, 2013, at 7:22 PM
To: Mila / From: Wes

First off, Mila, I can't tell you how much I appreciate this e-mail, and reading your words gave me a few butterflies I'd forgotten. I also think you're right about the challenges of communicating with people via e-mails and such, though, I firmly believe it's in part due to modern technology and the loss of effort people put into writing anymore.

I think back to when people had to hand-write letters and how much care, love, and effort one could put into words, a creative process that is lost in today's world for the most part. Having such accessibility in texting and e-mailing often makes us take our words for granted.

I realize how difficult all the sudden changes, good and bad, can be. Trust me, I've been doing it for the last seven years of my life. As weird as it might sound, I've come to enjoy the unpredictability of everything. It forces me to step back and really enjoy the present.

Don't feel guilty at all for this "roller-coaster ride." I don't regret a single minute of it. It allowed me to understand you better. It's in someone's worst that you typically get to see them for who they really are, and even with your faults, you're an amazing woman.

As for breaking up with me, I can't and do not hold that against you in any way. Looking in from the outside one would notice we barely know each other, having spent maybe a grand total of three weeks together in person. Though this was enough time to develop very strong feelings, it's no solid basis for a long-distance relationship.

That being said, I can't help but want to be in a relationship with you. There's something about you that I find nearly impossible to put into words, something that just makes me *feel* like I want you in my life. There's no easy logic to it. It's just a feeling that won't go away.

I can already detect positive changes in you through our texting. I can't wait to rediscover you when I come home … and I mean all of you, every inch of you. ☺

Love you,
Wes

TUESDAY, JULY 2, 2013

```
Mila: thanks for the sweet email
Mila: i appreciate ur understanding
```

Wes: ur welcome

Wes: what r u up to?

Mila: just work. u?

Wes: same. gettin ready for another trip

Mila: how long will u be gone?

Wes: not sure yet

Wes: pry a week or so

Wes: don't be surprised if it's longer
       though

Wes: don't want u to lose ur shit again ☺

Mila: haha very funny

Mila: i miss u ♥

Wes: miss u more babe ♥

WEDNESDAY, JULY 3, 2013

Wes: just taking off for another trip babe

Mila: okay, love. be safe

Wes: will do. happy early fourth, my lil
       firecracker

Mila: lol. happy early fourth, babe

FRIDAY, JULY 12, 2013

Wes: just stepped in the apartment mi amor

Mila: oh good! glad u made it back safely

Wes: me too!

Mila: i was just on my way out to the hot tub

Mila: [image attached]

Wes: wow

Wes: i think i now have a boner that's tall
enough to ride some of the scarier
rides at Elitch's

Mila: lol!! forget Elitch's … i'll give u the
ride of ur life ☺

Wes: ur so fuckin gorgeous. i want to rip
that sexy little swimming suit off u

Mila: [image attached]

Mila: like this?

Wes: fuck me

Mila: ☺

Wes: i can't wait to get my hands on u

Chapter 14

Subject: A story for you
Saturday, July 13, 2013, at 7:00 AM
To: Mila / From: Wes

Mi amor,

I have a little story I thought you might enjoy.

The Hitchhiker

Hank and I started today just like every other day. As the sun rose over the bay, we tossed on old running shoes and worked out before breakfast. Like usual, we raced to the top of the 1,500-foot hill left behind by the old gun battery and bunker that overlooks the ocean. The hill itself is relatively unpopulated with only two apartment buildings and a local family that lives in the old fort left over from war. It's not unusual to spot monkeys, sloths, and all kinds of other tropical creatures along the way.

We returned to our room, showered, and headed down to the truck for a busy day of tracking down needed mechanical parts. Hank started the truck and we began our lazy drive into town. As we drove, we noticed we were getting an unusual amount of attention for two gringos simply going to town. People were waving, pointing, and laughing directly at us. We assumed someone drew something inappropriate, like cock 'n' balls, in the dirt on the side of the truck as this is a normal prank for us guys.

Pulling over, we both jumped out and proceeded to walk around the truck looking for a giant dick drawn in the dust. Our search turned up nothing, and we both looked at each other in confusion. As we climbed back in the truck, we noticed a boy down the street pointing and laughing once again. This time (a little annoyed) we both jumped out for the second time, and as we reached the front of the truck noticed a pair of long claws and a grimy, fury head sticking out from under the bumper.

For the last five miles, a sloth had been hitchhiking!

As you know, sloths are known for their slowness. However, we quickly learned that once agitated they have a swiftness about them that would surprise most. We had to get him off the truck, so Hank and I fought this little creature with nearby resources, including sticks and a rubber hose. You'd laugh to know how long it took two well-trained and agile NSW guys to battle this critter. Eventually, I was able to grab it by the scruff of the neck and place it safely in a tree.

Typically, we search our vehicles for bombs or other disturbances … now we have to add sloths to that list!

I attached a video of the sloth battle for your viewing pleasure. ☺

Love,
Wesley Blackwell, the Sloth Subjugator

SATURDAY, JULY 13, 2013

```
Mila: holy shit! ur fucking hilarious
Mila: i just watched ur sloth subjugation
      video. i'm dying
Mila: my stomach hurts from laughing so hard
Wes:  haha! yeah that dirtbag didn't want to
      let go!
Mila: the attempt with the rubber hose …
      classic
Wes:  lol just being resourceful
Mila: i hear honey works better than vinegar
      … u shoulda lured it away with a piece
```

```
        of fruit or a bug or whatever it is a
        sloth eats
Wes:    this was no ordinary sloth babe. he was
        out for blood
Mila:   he just wanted a free ride
Wes:    there r no free rides in this world ☺
```

Subject: Contemplating a new path
Friday, July 26, 2013, at 10:15 PM
To: Wes / From: Mila

Hey sweetheart,

Sorry I haven't responded to any of your texts yet. I just got home from work. Shit really hit the fan today. I won't get into the boring details. Suffice it to say it had something to do with reviewing the midterm actuarial analysis performed by our independent third party. I had the pleasure of combing through a 150-page actuarial report. Oh joy!

You know, I've been seriously considering asking my boss if I can go part-time. I'm so tired of these vultures picking my carcass clean. I have no energy by the time I get home, and I'm sincerely trying SO HARD to improve myself. Work keeps getting in the way of my pursuit of positivity! I'm grateful for my job and the people I work with … I just want to work fewer hours. Is that so much to ask?

On another note, do you remember how nervous I was about moving home with my parents again (well, let's be honest, moving home with my *dad* again)? I thought it'd be a challenging transitioning from complete independence to living with my parents again. But it hasn't been. And I have to say, my dad and I seem to be getting along quite nicely since I moved in. It's been rather cathartic finally forming a bond with him, something I've yearned for my whole life. Forgiveness is a very powerful instrument of healing.

He has chilled out a lot in his older years. I still think he could stand to treat my mom a lot better, but he treats me great, and I've got to give him props for that. Also, knowing my dad is home and watching out for me, I can finally sleep peacefully, something I haven't experienced in years. When I lived alone, I slept so lightly, like a mother with a newborn child, waking to the slightest noises due to my paranoia. Now, I sleep deeply, feeling rested and energized when I wake.

Speaking of sleep, it's time to clock out.

Love you,
Mila

FRIDAY, JULY 26, 2013

Wes: u asleep yet?
Wes: just read ur email

Mila: just got in from the hot tub ☺

Wes: yum ☺ how was that?

Mila: wonderful. relaxing. almost fell asleep
out there with my meditative music lol

Wes: u know what kind of music would keep u
awake?

Mila: what?

Wes: the pork flute 😊 lol

Mila: oh my god.u pig lol

Wes: hahahahahahahaha i'm horny. haven't
gotten laid forever u know!

Mila: right there with u

Mila: i'd play one helluva tune on ur pork
flute right now. that's for sure ☺

Wes: lol i luv u

Wes: i think u should go part time babe

Wes: life is short. do what u need to be
happy

Wes: if ur happy, success will follow

Mila: thanks babe. i needed to hear that

Mila: idk why i've been dragging my feet on
this

Mila: i guess part of it is that i enjoy the
money

Mila: another part is that i love the status
of success

Mila: also i think i'm afraid they'll fire me
since it'd be easier than building a

```
            part-time position for me. i've never
            been fired before!
Wes:   who cares if they fire u! you'll find
            another job
Wes:   living with your parents gives u the
            perfect opportunity and financial free-
            dom
Mila:  ur right
Mila:  i'm gonna do it!
Mila:  it's time to make some changes!
Wes:   good. luv u babe ❣
Mila:  love u more ❣
Wes:   sweet dreams ☺
Mila:  goodnight handsome
```

Subject: Almost got fired today lol
Monday, July 29, 2013, at 6:48 PM
To: Wes / From: Mila

Hey babe,

So I totally almost got fired today! I sat down with my boss and explained to him that I wanted to go part-time. He was really disappointed but understood and told me he'd bring it up with his boss, our CFO.

In the end, they were both extremely disappointed but definitely wanted to keep me around for whatever amount of hours I'd be willing to work. The CFO wrote in an e-mail to me, "You know, Mila, zero percent of our professional staff have ever been allowed to go part-time. It's not something we want to offer to everybody, so we offer it to nobody. BUT since you're such an effective employee and since you've significantly improved the efficiency and profitability of the two companies you manage in the short period since January when we hired you, I'm going to go to bat for you on this one."

Not fifteen minutes later, and I received a call from the owner of RKD Holdings, and he fired me! Okay, he didn't really fire me, but he said I could either continue to work full time or I could quit. He didn't want other professional staff getting upset since apparently I'm not the only person who has asked to work part-time.

I was bummed, but I was prepared for it. About an hour later, I received a call from the CFO, and he tells me I can transition to a part-time position starting in two weeks. He said before he hung up, "I really stuck my neck out for you on this, Milena. Don't let me down." I promised him I would find a way to make it work for everybody.

I'M OFFICIALLY PART TIME (in two weeks, that is)! I'm ecstatic! It feels like a huge weight has been lifted off my shoulders today. I can finally stand up straight without all the pressure bearing down on me.

I'm going out with my parents for a celebratory dinner. Thanks for encouraging me to do this.

I love you,
Mila

MONDAY, JULY 29, 2013

```
Wes:   congrats on going part time babe ☺
Wes:   i'm proud of u
Mila:  thanks love. i feel so much relief and
       joy
Wes:   awesome! that's what i like to hear
Mila:  thanks for encouraging me wes … and for
       inspiring me to make some meaningful
       changes
Wes:   of course babe
Wes:   we're going fishing tomorrow (don't be
       mad)
Wes:   i'll email u when we get back
Mila:  sounds good. love u!
Wes:   luv u more ❣
```

Subject: Fishing shenanigans with the annoying girl from the embassy
Tuesday, July 30, 2013, at 7:52 PM
To: Mila / From: Wes

Hola mi amor!

Today, since we had a little free time, we decided to do a fun deep-sea fishing trip and invited some of the poor office embassy folk along for the ride. One of them is this CIA chick who's been particularly hard to work with and a real pain in our asses for a number of things. Unfortunately, we had to placate to some of her fucking idiotic requests ... so any opportunity we have to get even with her, you can bet we take full advantage.

Have you ever been big game fishing? I'm assuming you haven't. With big game fishing the fish are so big you typically "back down" on them, which means you back the boat up to the fish while it's being reeled in. We made a special request to the captain for this fishing trip, though!

The first fish that struck the line we handed the rod to our pain-in-the-ass lady coworker. While she was diligently fighting with and trying to reel the monster in, you could feel the ever so slight movement of the boat being put into gear. Not backward, as usual, but forward. I wish you could see the evil smirk on my face!

The twinkle in the captain's eye let us know this was gonna take a while. Fast-forward about an hour, and she's close to exhaustion. She's a tiny Asian woman and not cut out for this kind of physical work. She's been complaining of how tired her arm is and that she's cramping up, but we just continue to encourage her to reel in "her" fish. Finally, after we're happy with our exploits, we take the rod and remarkably reel the fish up to the boat with little to no effort somehow. Hahahahahaha! 😊

We ended up catching several good-sized tuna today. We were able to make it up to our Asian compadre by tossing her the fresh scraps from the tuna carvings. She snapped them up like a starving dog. She is Asian, after all, haha. In all seriousness, though, nothing beats fresh sushi!

Love you,
Wes

TUESDAY, JULY 30, 2013

Mila: just read ur email

Mila: lol. u guys r dickheads

Mila: that poor girl

Wes: haha i know but she deserves it

Mila: remind me to never get on ur bad side
      ☺

Wes: haha ☺

Wes: hey i just found out we gotta leave for
      another trip tonight

Mila: geez again?

Wes: yea gotta strike while it's hot

Mila: okie dokie. be safe.

Mila: love u lots ❣

Wes: luv u more ❣

Chapter 15

Subject: Indoor fishing
Sunday, August 11, 2013, at 6:13 AM
To: Mila / From: Wes

Mi amor,

Got back pretty late last night. Hank and I went to the local bar on the island to unwind from our trip, and for the first time this whole deployment I got fuckin' soused! Some of the fisherman and marina workers were celebrating something (I'm still not sure what), and Hank and I decided to join in on the festivities. I drank so much I blacked out at some point. I don't even remember coming home.

I woke up this morning to an interesting scene in our apartment. The first thing I saw when I walked into the living room was a fishing pole lying on the ground. The line had been cast and was tangled on the ceiling fan enough to make it completely useless for future use. There were charts, fishing tackle, beer bottles, and half-eaten food on the coffee table. Several pieces of furniture were out of place and/or knocked over.

Hank, upon hearing me, came out into the living room and smiled at my look of confusion. He said with a grin, "You went indoor fishing last night." Sadly, the only thing I caught was a killer hangover.

Love,
Your stupid boyfriend

TUESDAY, AUGUST 13, 2013

Mila: hey stupid boyfriend ☺

Mila: why am i not surprised u FISH when ur blackout drunk? 🐟 🐟 🐟!!

Wes: hey!

Wes: there u r

Wes: i haven't heard from u in a couple of days …?

Mila: i know. i'm sorry

Mila: i went camping with my family and ended up not having any service

Mila: just got back

Wes: camping sounds nice ☺

Mila: it was awesome 🌏

Mila: i'll send u some pics here in a bit

Wes: cool. i love pictures of you

Wes: naked

Mila: haha. get your mind out of the gutter

Wes: i miss u ♥

Mila: i miss u too ♥

Wes: got another trip this week

Wes: we leave tomorrow

Mila: boo

Mila: thanks for the heads up babe

Wes: i'm ready to come home and start camp-
       ing with u

Mila: we can share a sleeping bag ☺

Wes: naked 😊

Mila: lol can't wait!

Subject: Beneath the bell jar

Wednesday, August 28, 2013, at 10:11 PM

To: Wes / From: Mila

Hey babe,

It's been too long since I've talked to you. How's the trip?
Not sure when you'll be back, but I sure do miss you. It
feels like you've been gone longer than usual this time.

I've been thinking about you non-stop and writing helps quiet my mind a little.

I just got in from the hot tub. It's gorgeous outside. I saw three shooting stars! Isn't that something?! I know this sounds excessively romantic and kind of silly, but when I'm in the hot tub, I often look up at the stars and wonder if maybe you're looking at the same stars wherever you are. I like to imagine you are. It's comforting to feel some kind of connection with you, especially when we can't talk.

I've been reading some incredibly inspirational books lately. I forgot how much I love to read. Working the way I did, I usually left the office feeling picked clean to the bone of energy. By the time I found an hour or two for myself, I suffered from a serious case of mental anorexia, starved of any kind of productive reserve. I just wanted to smoke a bowl, sit in front of the TV, and shut my brain off for a while. Reading for enjoyment was a faraway luxury available only to people with time ... or perhaps to those who didn't exhaust their critical faculties at work.

I absolutely LOVE, LOVE, LOVE the extra freedom my part-time schedule affords me! For so long, I felt trapped beneath Sylvia Plath's "bell jar," choking on stale air, seeing only a distorted view of the world on the other side of the glass.

As it turns out (and no big surprise), time and freedom mixed with openness and willingness has proven to be an excellent concoction for mental and emotional healing. I can finally breathe again, Wes. I can finally see clearly again.

It was like with each new positive and healthy habit I endeavored to add to my daily routine, the bell jar cracked. Going part-time and focusing my new free time on positivity and well-being had the profound effect of adding so many cracks to the bell jar so abruptly, the glass finally shattered, and I'm no longer isolated in a world of sour, stinking air and distorted, warped phantasmagorias.

Of all the positive behaviors I've cultivated so far, reading inspirational books is by far the best. Like Matthew Kelly said, "Books really do change our lives, because what we read today walks and talks with us tomorrow."

Some people have the gift of saying things in a way that really resonates with others. It's not that the ideas in their books are new and ground-breaking. In fact, most of the ideas have been around since antiquity. The authors I've been reading recently, though, have somehow found the means to speak to me in a way that I can actually *hear* the message.

I think, though, the most important part aiding me in finally embracing the message is my *willingness* to hear it. A lot of the things I've been learning from my readings are the same things I know you and other people, like my parents and friends, have been trying to tell me all along.

Yet, being stuck beneath the bell jar, the messages came at me sounding distorted, more like reproachful criticisms than loving suggestions. When I was ready, nonetheless, my ears magically opened to the message. Like they say, "When the student is ready, the teacher will appear."

Having more free time also provides me the added benefit of pursuing other goals. Here is a list of some of my dreams:

* Become the healthiest version of myself
* Practice being more grateful and giving and living in the present moment
* Develop meaningful friendships
* Have a joyful marriage that lasts a lifetime
* Maintain the type of lifestyle that gives me ample freedom to do the things I love with frequency, like reading, writing, camping, walking, relaxing in the hot tub, meditating, etc., etc.
* Acquire a career that I love, one that allows me the freedom to be my own boss and contributes positively to society ... a job that fulfills my longing to make the world a better place
* Write a book that inspires people
* Invest in my future in all facets of life (financially, mentally, spiritually, and physically)
* Go scuba diving, swim with dolphins, make friends with a sea otter ☺
* Own a cabin and befriend a fox ☺

Tell me a little more about your future goals/plans.

Love you,
Mila

P.S. Steamy hot tub photo attached. ☺

Subject: To the woman who has successfully captured much of me I thought impossible
Saturday, August 31, 2013, at 10:12 AM
To: Mila / From: Wes

Mi amor,

Now *that* is the kind of e-mail I like to get upon returning from a long trip. Thank you for the awesome photo. I'm staring at it as I type. ☺ You're beautiful, Mila. Nothing sounds better right now than soaking in a hot tub with you wrapped in my arms.

As for my future interests, please forgive me for not doing this sooner. I've not withheld much from you, but I know I should be more transparent with the woman who has successfully captured much of me I thought impossible.

I get the sense you're anxious to settle down, start a family, and move in that direction ...? While there are some days I look forward to being a loving husband, a father, and having the idealistic loving family, to be honest, there are other days when I don't want those things.

This birthday was the first time in my life I felt old and got this eerie sense of not having enough time to do all the things I desire. I feel I have the opportunity to do great things in this world, Mila, even though how, when, and where elude me.

I've discovered I have an unquenchable thirst for knowledge, which is interesting considering my disdain for organized academics. My quest for adventure and travel is never-ending, and I enjoy both immensely. There are so many things I want to experience, do, and live that the thought of the stereotypical family isn't appealing to me. The white picket fence, some meaningless job, a cookie cutter house ... the list goes on. I know although I could find some happiness in that kind of life, I would not be fully content.

My only hope, then, is to find some kind of balance, to marry a woman who shares the same views, who isn't opposed to something other than the white picket fence, with whom to fully experience life. I'm honestly not very sure where your thoughts lie here, but my gut tells me you might want something that resembles the white picket fence ideal more than the other ...?

Even though I'm moving home this winter and away from active duty life, I will still be very much involved in our nation's military as a reservist. This is an area I feel I've been opaque with you ... only because I'm not even completely sure of my own feelings. A very strong part of me endeavors to pursue a path in the Army National Guard Special Forces based out of Colorado in three years or so if I can't find something else that has been as fulfilling as my current job. If this were to happen, then I'd be stationed and working in Colorado as part of a National Guard unit that is similar to the reserves in times of peace. Another part of me also feels that service in times of peace is a waste, and the majority of conflicts we involve ourselves with nowadays are not worth our lives or the money.

Lastly, I've always wanted to and have worked toward serving in what is called a Tier One unit. These are the men who routinely do missions you never hear about, but where the most good can be done. This is a dream I could and would sacrifice in times of peace and possibly having a family. What it comes down to is I don't see myself going back active unless it's truly needed or, if out of all the other things there are to do in this world, I can only find fulfillment in the military ... which is doubtful.

With the entirety of this running through my inefficient mind, I then have a very beautiful woman with incredible intelligence and a desirable personality who seems to like me even with all of my flaws. Her sincerity and loving ability are her most attractive qualities, quickly followed by her wit. She seems sort of lost at times, but has a good heart regardless. Few match her physical beauty, and one would be insane or simply incapable of love if he did not desire her. She is the object of my affections, my confusion, my longing, and my love. I feel that only time spent together will bring about what we are both searching for in answers.

I also wanted to include a list of some of my other goals (in no particular order).

* Own a small cabin in the mountains
* Own a catamaran and sail the world
* Create a successful business I enjoy and make enough money to support my goals and hobbies
* Get a master's degree
* Start taking martial arts classes again
* Get back to competitive shooting
* Take salsa lessons
* Learn how to play the piano
* The Ferrari, of course
* Become fluent in Spanish
* Be in great shape
* Find a companion in life who would be accepting of all of the above and participate in much of it

Also, I wanted to let you know I can't text you right now. The internet at my apartment is still out. It seems our landlord, a short, older Jewish gentleman, is in a vicious battle with the internet provider with no end in sight. He states he's switching companies, but who knows when that'll be accomplished. It's becoming rather a hindrance considering my constant use of the internet for homework, my startup business and everything in between. I'm sitting at a small café down the street from our apartment right now trying to get all my internet stuff done.

As far as work goes, it appears I'll be staying occupied until I head home. We're planning on doing a trip from Thursday to Saturday this week, and then numerous others until it's time to head home. It's been an easy and mostly enjoyable deployment compared to others. Nonetheless, I'll be glad to be done with all of this for a while.

One final thought I've been turning over in my head is a retreat I'd like to invite you to. It'll be in late October if they have it. I haven't received any information on it yet, but typically when returning from deployment, Naval Special Warfare does a retreat for the guys and their families. Last year it was from Friday until Sunday morning in Pensacola, Florida. I had a huge condo to myself, and it turned out to be pretty good decompression time. If the dates align and they're doing it this cycle, I'd like for you to go with me. It'd give us a chance to reconnect and give you a little better idea of my world over the last seven years.

Please tell me more about what you're learning from the books you're reading. "Books are the compasses and telescopes and sextants and charts which other men have prepared to help us navigate the dangerous seas of human life" (Dr. Jesse Bennett).

Sincerely yours,
Wes

Chapter 16

Mila: hey i'm glad u made it back safely

Mila: not sure if ur still at the café and will get these texts …

Wes: u caught me just in time ☺

Wes: i was just gettin ready to leave

Mila: yay! thanks for the email ☺

Wes: thanks for the steamy hot tub pic haha ☺

Mila: lol i figured that might tickle ur swickle pickle

Wes: tickle my swickle pickle?!

Wes: that's fuckin funny

Wes: i haven't heard that one before

Mila: lol i guess u could say i have a way
with words 😊

Wes: yep i luv it … nerd

Wes: so … befriend a fox huh? that's not
weird at all lol

Wes: and a sea otter?

Mila: yes!

Mila: i love foxes. they're my fav! 😊 🦊

Mila: foxes are way better than Ferraris 😊

Wes: not even close

Mila: and sea otters … well … they just seem
friendly … and cute 😊

Wes: ur a nut

Mila: lol i like animals

Wes: oh now it makes sense. that's why u
like me huh? … cuz i'm an animal in bed
😊

Mila: hahahahahahaha! yep u called it

Mila: goofball

Mila: i don't wanna hold u up babe. i'll
email u in a few days

Wes: can't wait 😊

Mila: love u ❣

Wes: luv u more ❣

Wes: my dirty lil sloot 😊

Subject: Manifesting my own reality
Tuesday, September 3, 2013, at 4:12 PM

To: Wes / From: Mila

Hey handsome,

First, allow me to cut to the pith. Yes, I've definitely been anxious to settle down. With that being said, over the last month or so, I've been starting to understand the root of my anxiety a little better. I'm no psychiatrist, but I imagine part of my anxiety stems from the fact that I worry I'll never be able to "keep" a man. This belief began to put down roots and spread its viney fingers after continuously losing men, whom I loved, to situations I felt were out of my control BUT were entirely within God's control. So, obviously, God was to blame since He was in control.

I've been foolishly sparring with God over this for a long time now. Quite immaturely, I've often pictured Him as this mean-spirited God who takes pleasure in dangling a carrot in front of my face, and then as soon as I get close enough to taste it, He rips it away again. This isn't the *only* thing I've been foolishly sparring with God about, but it's one of the bigger things.

As a response to this fear of never being allowed to "keep" a man, my not-so-logical logic tells me that marriage and starting a family is the solution to this problem—that if only I could marry a man and have a child with him, that I would, in essence, achieve my goal of "keeping" a man to love me and make me happy for a lifetime. This is, admittedly, in many ways a childish pre-occupation, but nevertheless, one that was bound with strings of steel through my steadfast misinterpretations of romance and how romance relates to my level of over-all satisfaction in life.

I'm slowly realizing that joy is not found in another human being. While others can certainly add to my happiness, they cannot be the source of it. The more I learn to care for myself, and the more I begin to respect myself and love myself, the less dependent I become on anyone else to fill the gaps in my heart. And in this process, I've learned to let go of my anxiety related to "keeping" a man as part of my life's fulfillment.

Don't get me wrong, I still very much desire marrying my soul mate, but if that never happens, I have no doubt that I will still lead an equally happy and fulfilling life, because, in the end, it is *I* who *chooses* to be happy and to do the things that make me feel fulfilled, regardless of my rela-tionships.

I really like what the spiritually enlightened mystic from India, Osho, has to say on the subject. (As a disclaimer, I don't know much at all about Osho or his "radical spiritual teachings," but I saw this quote floating around Facebook and took note of it.) Osho said:

"The capacity to be alone is the capacity to love. It may look paradoxical to you, but it is not. It is an existential truth: only those people who are capable of being alone are capable of love, of sharing, of going into the deepest core of the other person—without possessing the other, without becoming dependent on the other, without reducing the other to a thing, and without becoming addicted to the other. They allow the other absolute freedom, because they know that if the other leaves, they will be as happy as they are now. Their happiness cannot be taken by the other, because it is not given by the other."

Now, after readjusting my perspective, I imagine a healthy relationship involves people who know how to balance chiefly two things: 1) concentrating on personal fulfillment while; 2) maintaining the sagacity of selflessness.

On that note, when it comes to your future potential activity level in the military, honestly, I selfishly don't like it, BUT I'm learning to support it because I understand it brings you a sense of fulfillment, and everyone deserves that. You deserve "absolute freedom" to pursue the things in life you think are right for you. I never want to be your anchor, Wes. Rather, I want to be the woman who gives you wings. (Yes, I'm fully aware of how cheesy that sounds, thank you very much.)

Since meeting you, I'm discovering a side of me I was unaware of. You beckoned something forth from the recesses of my brain, some vital piece of me hidden in an overlooked corner. You summoned a sort of vague realization and drove it to the forefront of my mind. This realization prompted a series of thoughts that now nibble at me constantly. Thoughts that I cannot ignore. Thoughts that demand a different version of me.

I'm coming to understand that I have a wildness tucked inside me. Something fun and unpredictable and maybe just a little bit dangerous. ☺ I desire a life rich in new experiences. I've gotten a small taste of and have acquired a new appetite for risk and adventure. I'm now striving to push myself to live outside my comfort zone, to believe in myself beyond any latent ability I've previously demonstrated.

True, the white picket fence ideal used to be extremely appealing to me, but now I'm recognizing that it's not at all what I want, at least not right now. I'm no longer content to blend in. I long to live unconventionally, to live independently of the good opinion of others, to trust my inner voice and move confidently in the direction of *my* wildest dreams.

I, too, feel I'm destined for great things, though where, when, and how also elude me. I know I possess intelligence and talents I've yet to tap and unleash, and until I figure out what exactly it is inside of me that is so restless to make its impact on this world, hitting the pause button on the prospect of settling down and starting a family seems like the only sensible thing to do.

Now, as for the books I've been reading ... I'm eager to share the lessons I've learned not only with you, but with anyone and everyone who'll listen! And that's only because of the extraordinary impact I believe they've had on my own life. I'd love to pay it forward somehow and teaching others is one way I can do that.

One of the first books I picked up once I started on this new path in life (a now obvious moment of synchronicity, as the author would describe it) is a memoir by Dr. Wayne Dyer titled *I Can See Clearly Now*. Your mom actually gave me his name and told me to read some of his stuff.

To give you some background, Dr. Dyer began his career in the field of psychology. Being a very logical and pragmatic man, he was greatly moved by an experiment he witnessed as a psychology student that proved the undeniable power of thoughts over physicality. Essentially, the experiment demonstrated something similar to the placebo effect. It exhibited how our perceptual activity can be controlled by the beliefs we hold, and how the beliefs we hold are powerful enough to shape a physical reality.

Admittedly, he never intended his scientific quests to lead him on a spiritual journey, but alas, they did. The more he learned about the power of the mind, the more he nurtured new techniques to improve his own perceptions. He quickly became enthralled with his own success in changing his physical reality, what is known as the power of manifestation.

A lot of cynics believe this line of thinking (the power of manifestation) is New Age crap. Yet it isn't New Age at all. It existed since thousands of years before the teachings of Christ, through the teachings of Christ, and in many forms since then. There are inestimable real-life examples of its legitimacy.

The leap from understanding the power of the mind to spirituality is a pretty short one, although some people, even people very successful in the art of manifestation, don't make that leap, or at least not as concretely as Dr. Dyer did. Dyer discovered through his years of research and writing that being aligned with your "Source" (or God) is crucial for the success of manifesting your dreams *and finding fulfillment in the dreams you choose to manifest.*

As a side note, Dyer was reluctant to call your Source by common names like God because he knew many people would turn off their ears if they heard a name they immediately associated with religion like God, Allah, HaShem, etc. Dyer was not in the business of religion. He was focused purely on spirituality. They may seem like the same thing to a lot of people, but they're not. The distinction is an important one to me. I think this is one of the reasons why I found it so easy to connect with his writing. It goes back to my own reasoning from walking away from religion.

I have a tough time connecting to any one religion in its entirety because I feel like all religions get caught up in the details and frequently fail to see the forest for the trees. It's one of the major reasons why I stepped away from the Catholic faith. Like many religions, people of Catholicism are expected to conform to a certain set of beliefs and behaviors that are determined by higher clergies' interpretation of scripture. While many of their beliefs and rules of behavior naturally exist in my heart, many also do not.

I was the textbook "cafeteria Catholic" as they call them, going along picking and choosing which beliefs and rules of behavior I wanted to observe and leaving behind the rest. In the long run, I decided that I didn't want my faith associated with some of the beliefs served at the table of Catholicism. Certain philosophies served at that table I simply could not stomach, nor could I reconcile them with the values incarnated in my heart.

I liked how Dyer was not concerned with what you call the Source of your being or from which religious background, if any, you hail. His research spanned across all sorts of spiritual cultures, and there's one principle that weaves itself through the core of the greatest spiritual teachings. And that is the following: the supreme ethic of life is love.

Okay so this e-mail is getting ridiculously long. Sorry about that! I can talk about this stuff all day. Still, I need to wrap it up here so I can go workout, eat dinner, and then soak in the hot tub! Here is a summary of the main points Dr. Dyer makes about what he finds to be the most effective and beneficial steps of manifestation.

1. Like I said, first you must be aligned with your Source. Or said differently, you must be aligned with the Supreme Ethic of Love.
2. You must be impervious to your culture and all the opinions society and well-intended loved ones "brainwash" you with. Never let anyone or anything but your highest-self direct your attention.
3. You must be willing to change your concept of the power of your thoughts and beliefs.
4. You must recognize that you are a creation made in the likeness of the Creator, therefore, you possess the inherited ability to create things out of nothing.
5. You must be grateful and giving and continually assess your alignment with your Source.
6. It's important to fuel your imagination. You must not only visualize your desires but *feel* the feelings you would have as if they were a present reality.
7. To take this even a step further, you must live as if what you desire already exists like your prayer has already been answered. Think of this as an act of pure faith.

Yep, that's the gist of it. There's so much more to say on the subject, but at least this summary gives you an idea of some of the stuff I've been reading. I realize this is probably not new information to you. Only an ocean of ink has been spilled extolling these philosophies LOL! I'd be willing to bet you've read similar types of ideas, perhaps presented in a different context.

Last but not least, I would love to join you on the post-deployment retreat if you happen to go again.

Love,
Mila

P.S. I'm sorry to hear about your internet. I miss your texts.

———————————————————————————————

Subject: Holy e-mail!
Wednesday, September 4, 2013, at 5:31 AM
To: Mila / From: Wes

Mi amor,

I gotta say, I don't think I've ever been more attracted to you than I am now ... and that's saying a lot since I've seen you naked!

You know how you get all fuckin' irritated with me for telling you "it'll be fine" all the time? Haha. ☺ Well, I think you've caught on by now that's my mantra, and that's just how I feel about everything. I don't say it to be an asshole ... well, sometimes I do, but really I say it because I just don't fret about things. When I say "it'll be fine" I'm not saying everything will turn out the way I want it to. I'm saying no matter how things turn out, I know it'll be fine.

It's actually an expression of my faith. God is in complete control, and because I have total faith in Him and in His plan, it'll always be fine. Even if I'm dead, I promise you, it'll be fine.

To me, faith's not about me believing everything'll turn out fine in the human understanding of the word. God's wisdom and His plan are much too big for my tiny pea brain to comprehend. Faith is about being okay no matter how things turn out. Do you see what I'm saying?

Having faith to this degree is very freeing, Mila. It relieves unnecessary stress and provides a deep sense of peace. Obviously, it's in our human nature to worry about things. If we don't have anything big to worry about, we worry about the stupidest fuckin' shit. Big or little, worry is always a waste of energy, and the root of worry is mistrust in God.

I think it's great you're discovering the root of your anxiety, especially when it comes to settling down. I think deep down you've known all along it wasn't the right thing for you to do at this point, otherwise, you would've done it already by now. There are only about a zillion guys out there who'd be willing to marry you today if you really wanted to!

The wild girl tucked inside of you is wildly attractive, Mila, and she deserves a chance to make more of the choices. Personally, I think she makes better choices, and by that I mean more authentic ones.

I first witnessed the wild side of you on our first date when you all but raped me in my sleep. There was no way I could stop myself from falling in love with that free-spirited part of you. And don't you dare misinterpret me— I'm not saying I fell in love with you because you were sluttin' it up! Haha ☺ I'm saying I fell in love with you because I knew you were acting honestly on what you deeply desired, despite all of the external influences in your life telling you not to. You acted on what *you* felt was right. Not what some religious organization told you to do, not what society told you to do, and not what the guarded, distrusting, pained part of you told you to do. You and I both know our connection that night transcended merely a physical one. There was something powerful working over both of us, and it will forever be a memory I cherish.

Your e-mail brought back to life that girl I fell so hard for, and I think that's why I'm so deeply attracted to you right now. I feel like this is the real you.

You said in your previous e-mail, "I did not want my faith associated with some of the beliefs served at the table of Catholicism." What beliefs are you referring to?

I've never read any of Dyer's books, but like you guessed, I've read a lot of books that cover similar topics. Isn't it kind of fucked up to think how many books exist on the topic and yet so many people still seem oblivious to it? Take you for example. You're evidently smart, even read books on the subject while in college and, yet, you still didn't really *get it* until now. You learned it, but you never *knew* it. It's like you said about the necessity of the student being ready to hear the message, then the teacher will appear. I think the only reason you opened up to it is because you were forced out of your moderately comfortable zone of mediocrity into someplace much more uncomfortable.

I'm sorry I can't mirror the length of your previous e-mail. I have a lot more to say and would love to keep writing, but we're super busy getting ready for our trip tomorrow and I need to help the guys pack up.

Love you,
Wes

Chapter 17

Subject: "Re-examine all you have been told ... Dismiss what insults your soul."
Sunday, September 8, 2013, at 7:13 PM
To: Wes / From: Mila

Hey handsome,

You're totally right about why I decided to make a serious change in my life. When I finally sagged outside of my "moderately comfortable zone of mediocrity" into someplace much more uncomfortable, I could no longer push my plights off to another day or mask them with more marijuana. The lightbulb finally came on, and I realized my attempts at treating the symptoms were doing nothing to cure the core problem. Had I not been forced out of my grayish comfort zone into someplace darker, I'm afraid I could've gone on like that my entire life. It reminds me of the quote by Helen Keller: "Character cannot be developed in ease and quiet. Only through experience of trial and suffering can the soul be strengthened, ambition inspired, and success achieved."

Keller's famous saying reminds me of when I was growing up. In response to challenging times, my mom's go-to phrase was "it builds character." This annoyed me at the time because it seemed kind of calloused when I just wanted her sympathy; also I wasn't super interested in building more character. I thought I had plenty of that, which is just laughable to think about now.

What I know now is that challenge alone doesn't build character. Hardship only builds character if I suck it up and decide to make the right choices even though the situation is painful or unfair.

Unfairness has been a theme of conflict for me over the past few years. "Losing" you to your deployment was just one of many things I felt was unfair, and it sent me plundering down a path of self-pity and resentment. Your deployment just happened to be the straw that broke the camel's back.

Most of my anger at life (and God) was sown by the seeds of unfairness. I thought life should be about granting the fair reward for the right performance. Yet, the more I lived, the more I realized how unfair the world is. I didn't like it nor did I understand why an all-powerful, loving God allowed it. Why can't fairness be a feature of our world?

Unfortunately, I understand there is nothing fair about a broken world full of broken people. Likewise, there is nothing fair about the gifts of grace and forgiveness.

My first step in healing was letting go of my need for fairness.

Looking back, I'm ashamed of how unfair I thought my situation was. Now that I've poked my head above the negative smog that clouded my dreary world, I'm unbearably humiliated to admit I ever had thoughts like that. There are so many people in this world with real problems. I'm ashamed to think how I've been behaving and the ungracious thoughts I've been brewing.

Instead of beating myself up about it, though, I've decided to be grateful for and humbled by the hardship and the lesson. I've accepted that sometimes your perceived enemy is your friend.

You asked about the things that ultimately drove me away from the Catholic Church, and in doing so, you unintentionally opened a can of worms. There is no short, simple answer to that question. Leaving the Catholic Church was a big deal to me. It was a BIG deal to my whole family, and you know I'm very close with them, so I'm sure you can imagine that it wasn't something I took lightly. But I had to do it. I felt called by God to do it, and that's just the honest truth.

I'm going to preface this next portion of my e-mail with the following: I believe there's a lot of good that can be accomplished via religion. I'm appreciative for many aspects of my Catholic upbringing, for the numerous life lessons I learned and relationships I built in that community. I don't harbor any negative feelings toward the Catholic Church or its followers.

That being said, there're many things about the Catholic faith I cannot reconcile in my heart. For example, one of the bigger disagreements I have with Catholicism is its position on homosexuality. The Catholic Church believes that acts of homosexuality constitute mortal sins, the types of sins that are fatal, or deadly to heaven.

I believe gay people have just as much right as any other human being on the face of this planet to experience love and romance and marriage and family. Some of the most beautiful-spirited people I know are gay, and I could never believe they're acting in sin merely because they desire the same gifts from God I desire. People have no more control over their sexuality than the color of their skin. Like I've said before, the supreme ethic of life is love. I believe as long as we are acting in love, we are acting in God. Period.

I also strongly disagree with the necessity of confession with a priest in order to absolve the soul of mortal sins. Last time I checked, I didn't need an intermediary to ask God for forgiveness and to receive it. I'm guessing you don't know much about the Catholic religion, so here's a quick lesson on mortal vs venial sins. Mortal sins are considered to be deadly to heaven, or said differently, are considered to hold the power to send you to hell if not confessed to a priest before you die. Venial sins are less serious and are not required to be confessed to a priest in order to be forgiven.

I don't think there is anything wrong if you feel compelled to confess your sins to a priest or a friend or whomever if it makes you feel better. Also, I believe in the power of humiliation as well as accountability in discouraging us from committing sins in the future. What I disagree with is the NECESSITY of confession with a priest in order to absolve the soul. To me, this requirement is unsubstantiated, and I think it sends the wrong message to people. I think it separates people from a personal, intimate connection with God by requiring a human intermediary for an act that is, by nature, incredibly personal and private.

These represent merely two examples of a multitude of things I disagree with that the Catholic Church preaches. I'm stopping at two because otherwise this e-mail might go on for days, and I'd probably bore the shit out of you!! LOL. If asked to summarize my main point of contention with Catholicism it would be that religion in general, not just Catholicism, is kind of close-minded. Religion frequently ends up dividing more people than it unites. Or maybe that's just my experience of it?

I remember when I was a little girl, everything in the world fell into either one of two categories: wrong or right. That's what I was taught. Now that I'm an adult, I understand that while there are some things that fall into those two categories, most things don't. Most things aren't wrong, aren't right, aren't black, aren't white. Most things are just different. And unless you've experienced them personally, you cannot understand or judge them.

I believe my Source of Being communicates with my spirit directly, and I always know, deep down, whether I'm acting morally—notwithstanding the sad fact that I sometimes go to great lengths to try to deceive myself and turn away from my inner light. I'm very slowly learning to trust the wisdom I have inside me. And I'm finding that when I do, a river of joy flows within me. As Dr. Dyer paraphrased the ancient teacher Lao-Tzu who wrote in the Tao Te Ching, "When the greatness of the Tao (God) is present, action arises from one's own heart. When the greatness of the Tao is absent, action comes from the rules."

I hope you had a good "trip," and you're traveling home safely as I write this to you.

With lots of love and humility,
Mila

P.S. I'm sorry if some parts of this e-mail came across a little preachy or whatever. I know people come from different walks of life and may have a completely different experience of religion than myself. I'm not trying to be persuasive. I'm only trying to help you understand why I made the decision I did. It was an important one for me, so I wanted to be clear.

Subject: Feeding frenzy
Monday, September 9, 2013, at 8:27 AM
To: Mila / From: Wes

Mi amor,

I'm sitting inside the boat right now on our way back. It's a beautiful day but the seas are not the most comfortable at the moment. We had a pretty good trip and were able to do some fishing in our downtime. We came across a feeding frenzy of tuna this morning and were able to get about three on board. Hooked a bunch more, but the sharks ate them before we could pull them into the boat. I'm looking forward to getting back to the apartment. Hopefully I'll be able to send this e-mail this evening if the internet is working.

It's hard to believe this deployment is almost over already. Only a little over a month left. This deployment, compared to others, has been flying by extra fast for me. I can't believe it'll be my last one for a while. Sometimes I'm nostalgic just thinking about it.

Who else gets to hang out with their best friends, do awesome shit, and get paid for it? The brotherhood of this type of team is hard to put into words and hard to find in any other kind of relationship. I think that's what I'll miss the most. The guys I work with are my best friends and my brothers. We trust each other with our lives and with some of our deepest secrets, which we are bound to share with no one else in the world. We share extreme highs and lows with each other in our adventures and losses. I doubt I'll ever build the same connection with other people in "normal" circumstances. I'm gonna miss the shit out of these guys.

Okay, so I gave up trying to write this on the boat, damn thing was rocking too much and near impossible to type and read on there. We got back home last night, and I was absolutely exhausted. We made the mistake of stuffing ourselves full of pizza before bed, and my stomach is paying for it now. Something about how they make pizza down here really destroys our stomachs ... it just tastes so good!

As for what you wrote in your e-mail about fairness, I think a lot of people get hung up on that. But you're right, this world is anything but fair. You know what I think one of your other hang-ups is? Fear. I think you're a fearful person, and I think I get why. You felt a lot of fear growing up between all the domestic violence and the weird stalker and whatnot. Fear has been a useful emotion for you in many ways, especially when it came to protecting yourself. But I'm a firm believer that fear is one of the most debilitating emotions out there.

"Fear causes you to feel small and powerless. Fear is the most insidious and suffocating emotion. How many great and beautiful people have withered and vanished—whose gifts the world never knew—because of fear's dread? Fear is paralyzing to life. When we are afraid of failure, judgment, loneliness, or rejection, we try to play it safe to avoid fear's pain and uncertainty. When we are afraid, we advance cautiously and try to keep things the same and 'safe.' ... It can be so hard to face our fears. It is a pathetic agony, so desperately wanting to liberate our dreams and live fully and completely in alignment with our hopes. It feels like crawling when we want to stand

and leap. Yet, with all the passion, hope, faith and determination we can muster, we still feel the foreboding unease that our dreams, if attempted, could become a nightmare. This is how we are stunted by fear. Fear is a thief because it robs you before you even begin." —Bryant McGill

Didn't you say you became an accountant because you *feared* the crashing economy wouldn't support your dream of becoming a writer? Now that you're working part-time, maybe it's time to dare to write that book you've been dreaming about. From the length of your e-mails, it seems like you've got plenty to say. ☺ I love reading your words, Mila. I'm sure others would, too.

I think you and I see eye-to-eye on the topic of religion for the most part. I'm probably a little less diplomatic and a little more blunt about it, but I like the way you describe your reasoning of being open-minded and pursuing a commitment to limitless love. I have something to learn from you in that department!

Basically, I see religion as a "brood of vipers." I don't think many religious people are very far removed from the hypocrites and Pharisees of ancient times, which is exactly one of the things Jesus was out to eradicate.

Honestly, I've not put much thought into religion since I don't care to fit the bill. There is probably a lot of good that goes along with it, but I've also seen the underbelly of it. I've dealt with extremists in Iraq, and I'll tell you right now, I never hesitated to take one of those evil fuckers out. Not even for a second.

Love,
Wes

P.S. I'll send you some pictures of the fish we caught here in a bit. Just need Hank to download them from his camera.

Chapter 18

Subject: Pilfering from sharks?! Bold move.
Monday, September 9, 2013, at 7:16 PM
To: Wes / From: Mila

Hey babe,

Love the pictures! Thanks for sending them. I nearly forgot how handsome you are. I'm drooling over here! Fishing must've been a lot of fun. That sailfish was insanely large!! You didn't mention pulling that monster on board. It could eat me I'm pretty sure... also, I must add—it's a little disturbing sharks were eating the tuna right off your hooks. I have this image of you taking one wrong step and slipping overboard, becoming instant lunchmeat. Pilfering from sharks is a bold move, my love. ☺

In reply to what you said about fear being one of my hang-ups—yeah, I agree. I am a fearful person. I do think part of my fearful disposition was learned in my youth and was a product of my environment, but I also know now that I'm guilty of fanning the flames of my fears over the years. In one of the books I read recently there was a quote from Aristotle. He said, "many bodily feelings in humans ... are caused by the way humans view the world around them." This made sense to me because I frequently viewed the world around me as harsh and unfair, absent of a good God, and lacking purpose. My focus was often on the overabundance of evil in this world, rather than the plethora of good.

In the beginning, I prayed my little heart out, but my prayers were never answered (or so it seemed). Eventually, I stopped praying. Think of it this way, if someone constantly ripped a chair out from underneath you, sooner or later you'd stop trying to sit down.

Over time, the further I drifted from God, the more I acquired the kind of perspective that encouraged my negative emotions to run rampant—a tremendously corrupting phenomena. Now I'm in the process of building a new perspective focused on positivity, hope, and love. It's not easy. Sometimes I feel like I'm lying to myself.

Most often, though, I witness a change in my life for the better.

A little over a month ago I started getting coffee every week with a friend of mine from the past. As youngsters we became good friends through our church catechism program. I lost touch with her after I graduated and moved to Denver, but we recently reconnected. Her name is Zelie.

Remember our conversation about unfairness? Well, let me tell you a little bit about Zelie. Her story is a spirited defiance of one of unfairness's more mistreated victims.

When her mom was in the process of giving birth to her, the doctors had to pull her out with forceps but something went wrong, causing Zelie to have a stroke. This was the origin of certain medical challenges for her, namely cerebral palsy and epilepsy.

All through her youth, Zelie attended speech, physical, and occupational therapy classes. She and her parents worked hard to reverse some of the damage caused to her brain in infancy. To this day, reading is a challenge for Zelie because her eyes become strained, making her tired and sometimes giving her headaches. Yet I frequently see her down at the coffee shop with a chai latte in hand and a Bible resting open on the table in front of her.

Because of the epilepsy, Zelie cannot have a driver's license. Unfortunately, it's too dangerous for her and others since she could have a seizure with little or no warning while on the road. Yet Zelie is very self-sufficient. She rarely asks anyone to take her anywhere. She has mindfully situated her life so she can walk to work, the store, and other amenities of necessity.

She works in Wheatland at an assisted living/nursing home. Periodically we walk to the coffee shop which is conveniently located right up the street from my parents' house and across the street from her work.

Zelie is one of the most inspirational people I know. She is incredibly loving, spiritual, and positive. One thing I really like about her is that she is completely nonjudgmental. Even while she lives life very piously in an impious world, she does not pass judgment on other people for living their lives much less graciously (like me!). It's a very beautiful thing to be embraced by such unconditional love.

She's really got life figured out, you know? She doesn't measure her life's success by how far she goes in her career or how much money she has in her bank account or how many people on Facebook envy her or any of the other things many of us overvalue in our society. Zelie measures the success of her life by how many people she can share her love with.

Needless to say, she's opened my eyes and, in doing so, has had an exceptionally positive impact on my life without even knowing she was doing it. If ever I start to feel sorry for myself, all I have to do is think about all of the high hurdles Zelie has had to jump over, every single one of them with physical disabilities. When I look at her and witness how she courageously carries her heavy cross, I'm deeply humbled and reminded of all of my blessings and of how I've taken them for granted over the years.

I think her situation particularly hits home because when my mom was giving birth to me, the doctors had to pull me out with forceps, too. I could've easily been in Zelie's shoes. If I'm capable of being a negative person even with all of my abundant blessings, I shudder to think what I would've been like had the roles been reversed.

I hate to confess this about myself, but somewhere along the line I started judging my place in this world from a superior position, like I was "Boettcher" than everyone else. I've always felt smarter than other people and more beautiful than most. I passed it off as having "confidence" in my blessings, but now I'm seeing it for what it really was: conceitedness.

Truth is like that sometimes. It's hidden in a hallway of mirrors. You think you see it, but you're really seeing a slanted, distorted reflection of it. I always thought I was smart enough to identify the real thing. But what is intelligence deprived of a double dose of wisdom? I tell you what it is. It's dangerous.

My friendship with Zelie, unbeknownst to her, has had the profound effect of exposing many of the deceptions I've viewed as truths over the years and, in return, has motivated me to work on myself more. It's astonishing how many teachers exist in this world once you open your eyes to them!

My heart is changing, Wes. Slowly but surely, my heart is changing! ☺

As for writing a book ... I have no idea what I would even write about. Still, I know there is a book inside me, itching to make its way out.

Love,
Mila

Subject: [None]
Tuesday, September 10, 2013, at 10:59 PM
To: Mila / From: Wes

Babe,

Guess I shouldn't tell you the part where I was debating whether or not to jump in the water and do some spearfishing for tuna. The first head-only fish we brought up changed my mind! We ended up hooking one shark and even though he was small, just a six-foot bull shark, they're notorious for being aggressive.

I'm happy to hear about your friendship with Zelie. She sounds like a great girl. It's old school advice, but that's only because the truth of it stands the test of time: choose your friends wisely. I'm glad you're building some inspiring friendships. That was one of the goals you listed in a previous e-mail.

What have you been reading lately?

Sorry to cut this e-mail short, babe. There are some work-related things that are weighing heavily on my mind right now. I wish I could talk to you about them, but I can't. I'll touch base with you later.

Love,
Wes

Subject: You okay?
Wednesday, September 11, 2013, at 9:15 AM
To: Wes / From: Mila

Hey love,

You okay? You were obviously distracted in your last e-mail, and I haven't heard from you since. I wish you could tell me what's going on. Sometimes it's so difficult for me to accept that there's a side to your life I know nothing about.

Anyway, I just finished up a really good book called *The Shack*. The premise of the book is intriguing. A father took his two children camping. His son accidentally flipped a little canoe on the lake, sucked up a bunch of water into his lungs, and started to drown. The father saw this happen and swam out to his aid. While he was saving the life of his son, his youngest daughter sat coloring at the picnic table when a man abducted her. The book soon revealed that the man who abducted the young girl brutally murdered her in an abandoned shack.

The father struggled for years trying to process the unspeakable amount of pain he endured because of this tragedy. His marriage struggled, and understandably, his relationship with God suffered. He was a man who attended seminary school in his youth and took pride in his solid relationship with God. The way his faith was shook surprised him and his family.

Ultimately, it's a striking story of forgiveness. In many ways, it helped restore bits and pieces of my own faith.

Apparently, there are a lot of critics out there who've gotten worked up about this book. I can appreciate why it might be upsetting to some people, whether because of the subject matter (the brutal murder of an innocent child) or because of some of the book's theological implications (God's portrayal as a black woman).

I personally loved that this book was unconventional in its theological implications, though. It was meant to shatter our limited perspective of God. And I believe it does so beautifully.

The story was not only a journey of forgiveness, but it was a lesson in building an intimate relationship with God. It's easy to treat God more like a professional counterpart than a good buddy. For me, I never wanted to disrespect God by treating Him too casually. I learned in my youth that God is to be revered, worshiped, and even feared. *The Shack* offers the balancing side of that equation where God is "Papa" and He/She is a jokester, a fun friend, and someone relaxed and easy to talk to about anything.

I think I'll start calling God "Papa" too. It has a nice ring to it.

Anyhow, I'm really sorry if all my spiritual stuff is boring!! I realize I've been talking about it a lot lately. It's on my mind constantly because it's something I'm working on.

Love,
Mila

WEDNESDAY, SEPTEMBER 11

Wes: thank u for the email sweetheart

Wes: don't apologize for ur spiritual rants lol

Wes: i find them interesting … mostly because they help me understand u better

Mila: i prefer u call them "The Mystical Musings of Mila" rather than "spiritual rants" lol ☺

Wes: haha

Mila: u okay babe?

Mila: ur last email was so short

Wes: yea just dealing with some tough stuff

Wes: it'll be fine ☺

Mila: lol i shoulda guessed

Wes: besides wouldn't want to pass on some of this stuff to u

Mila: u know u can talk to me about anything

Wes: i know but i wouldn't want to

Wes: it'd be kinda like stealing a child's innocence unnecessarily

Mila: i think u already stole my innocence ☺

Wes: lol yea maybe … but in an awesome way

Mila: i miss u ♥

Wes: me too babe ♥

Wes: ur not gonna like this but we're gonna do one big final push before we head home

Wes: i'll be outta reach for at least a
       month

Wes: pry won't hear from me until i'm headed
       back to the states

Mila: ☹

Mila: at least ur coming home soon

Wes: also got word they aren't doing the re-
       treat for us when we get back

Mila: bastards!

Wes: oh well lol

Wes: will u come out and stay on my boat
       with me for a bit?

Wes: i can show u the base where i work when
       i'm not deployed

Mila: i'd love that

Wes: we can even spend a few nights in New
       Orleans if u want

Mila: i don't really care what we do as long
       as i'm with u ☺

Wes: same here

Wes: i luv u more than u know mila

Mila: i love u too ❣

Mila: i'm so excited to be with u again!

Wes: u won't even be able to walk after i'm
       done with u ☺

Mila: don't u threaten me with a good time ☺

Wes: haha catch u on the flip side mi amor

Mila: i'll be counting the days ❣

Chapter 19

O ver the next month I continued to take matters of self-improvement seriously and could feel myself growing stronger. I improved physically, mentally, and spiritually.

There was one part of me, though, that wasn't getting any healthier: my skin. Specifically the skin on my face. I started to develop unsightly flesh-colored bumps on my cheeks. They didn't look inflamed, red, or tender like acne, yet if I squeezed them, a thick pus-like substance would come out.

The bumps wouldn't go away regardless of whether I squeezed them or didn't touch them, so I made an appointment with a dermatologist. She examined my skin and recommended a gentler face wash, a professional microdermabrasion and chemical peel treatment, and prescription strength retinol cream. I started the treatment plan that very day, yet the bumps only seemed to grow larger and multiply in number no matter what I did.

I tried everything I could think of to fix the problem before Wes came home. The bumps were terribly embarrassing, but I understood that stressing about them would only exacerbate the problem. I tried to stay positive as best I could.

My exhaustive internet research told me that whatever was wrong with me needed to be treated from the inside, too, not just on the surface. So I changed my diet to avoid dairy and foods with a high glycemic index. I ate foods known to support the health of the skin like avocados, oatmeal, bell peppers, kidney beans, etc. I upped my dosage of vitamins just in case my restrictive diet somehow prevented me from consuming the necessary nutrition my body required.

As a provisional measure, I switched to all-natural, organic face products should the bumps be an allergic reaction to the host of chemicals in the products I used beforehand. I not only swapped my face products, but I also replaced my laundry detergent, shampoo, conditioner, body wash, and lotion. I did everything in my control. And nothing helped.

❧

FRIDAY, OCTOBER 11

Wes: I'M HOME!!!!!!!!!!!!!!!!!!!!!!!!!!

Mila: yyyyyyyyyyyyyyyyeeeeeeeeeeeeeeeeeeeeee
       sssssssssssssssssssssssss!!!

Mila: like back in the states home or back to
       your apartment in Panama home?

Wes: back in the states

Mila: for real?! yay!

Wes: may i book u a flight to come see me?

Mila: yyyyyyyyyyyyyyyyeeeeeeeeeeeeeeeeeeeeee
       essssssssssssssssssssssssss!!!

Wes: when can u come?

Mila: now!… whenever ☺

Mila: honestly i'll make any date work

Wes: ok i'll email u the flight info in a
       couple hours ☺

Mila: thanks! i'm so glad ur finally home
       babe

Wes: me too!

Wes: can't wait to see u

Mila: me either!

Mila: love u! ☺

Wes: luv u more!!!!!! ☺ ☺ ☺

Less than 24 hours later, I buckled my seatbelt while only sort of watching the flight safety video on a small monitor in front of me. My palms sweated with excitement, and I kept nervously wiping them on the scant fabric of my sexy, way-too-short jean skirt. Even though drinking alcohol wasn't "my thing," I ordered a gin and tonic the first chance I got.

As the plane took off, I could tangibly feel the miles between us shrinking. With each mile and sip of my drink, I decompressed a little, as if Wes and I were at two ends of some invisible elastic strand, and the pressure relieved itself the closer we got.

When the flight landed, I grabbed my carry-on and immediately made my way to the restroom to freshen-up some before heading to the baggage terminal. I tried to apply more makeup to disguise the unattractive bumps on my cheeks, but it was useless. Nothing short of a full facemask could hide those hideous things.

Wes stood waiting for me near the terminal. I spotted him before he spotted me. He has the kind of arrestingly handsome face that becomes instantly visible in a crowd.

I stopped in my tracks, drinking him in. He wore tactical sunglasses pushed up on the top of his head, a forest green T-shirt, khaki shorts, and flip-flops. I noticed practically every woman within viewing range stealing glances at him. The men were, too. Tan, muscular, standing tall with the identifiable posture of a soldier, how could one not look at him? He was perfect.

Wes's eyes professionally scanned the crowd with military precision, presumably taking note of details most people wouldn't see. And then his eyes—those turbulent, lusty-for-life eyes—locked on me.

For a brief instant, neither of us made a move. We just stared, smiling. Memories waterlogged my brain while momentarily drowning my cognitive abilities. I couldn't think or simply reason to take a step toward him. All I could do was remember the last time he looked at me that way, the vision clear as glass in my memory. He had a way of looking at me that changed my whole world.

My knees weakened. My heartbeat thickened. I dropped my carry-on to the ground beside me, trying not to fall with it. I felt like Gumby, with rubber limbs I wasn't convinced would support me. I didn't dare move. He jogged to my side and slid his hands around my waist, unburdening my need to stand strong. I let my whole weight lean into his solid grasp.

Without saying a single word, he bent over and kissed my forehead, then under my eye, then my nose, and then my cheek. He moved across my face, taking the long way to my mouth. Once there, he kissed me much longer than is really polite in public.

Meanwhile, one of his hands dropped to the bare skin of my thigh and, as if by reflex, slid under my skirt and tucked itself just under my behind, threatening to bear my already scarcely-covered backside to onlookers.

"What the hell," I asked, politely, "do you think you're doing?" My lips grazed his as the words exited my mouth. Wes, as if just now realizing we weren't alone in our own secluded and hidden world, smiled at me sheepishly and placed his wandering hand in my own.

I must admit, though, it was kind of true. We were standing in our own bubble of time where things moved in a blur around us and the only thing in focus was each other.

"My bad," he said. He plainly didn't mean it, though, as evidenced by his widening grin and twinkling eyes which were attractively crinkled in the corners.

He pulled me in for another long, soft, sweet kiss. He took his time when he kissed me. There was no hint of urgency in the way his tongue slipped between my lips and traveled around my mouth. My pulse scrambled. A hot, tingling sensation started in my toes and soon worked its way through my entire body, leaving my limbs almost numb with heat. I could feel people looking our direction and the color deepening in my cheeks.

"I missed you," I purred as he repositioned his lips at a new angle over mine.

"I missed you more," he rejoined, his breath steamy on my face.

"Shall we get your luggage?" He asked after kissing me for several more seconds.

"Yes," I answered quietly, feeling out of breath.

I bit my lower lip, smiling, as we walked together with his thumb tucked in my belt loop and my carry-on over his shoulder. He effortlessly pulled my heavy luggage off the conveyer belt, and we made our lazy way to his car.

Then something strange happened.

Something happened I don't think I'll ever fully understand, even though I obsessively dissected the moment countless times after the fact.

When we climbed into the car, just the two of us sitting in silence and privacy for the first time in almost a year, neither of us knew what to say. Something changed in that moment. It was a small shift but a decisive one. A sliver of invisible foreignness, or some kind of unfamiliarity, crossed between us, and suddenly the magic bubble burst.

Things got awkward. Fast. It was like we barely knew each other, yet we had traded thousands upon thousands of words and intimate details expressing our deepest selves over the last eight months. We grappled in haste for some kind of small talk just to fill the silence.

In the meantime, a horrible thought entered my mind. *What if our e-mails had created some kind of false intimacy between us?* The clumsiness of our conversation unpleasantly reminded me, again, that I hardly knew this person in the flesh.

Didn't we know each other by now, though? We had exchanged enough words to fill the pages of an entire novel. We'd been a couple for the better part of a year. We'd been talking for almost three. Yet something was missing. There seemed to linger some sort of inexplicable sense of things being not quite right.

Later, many months after our reconnection, I recognized that our e-mails had, in fact, shaped a type of false intimacy without either of us meaning it. There happens to be an equation to intimacy, and we lacked one of the fundamental components. Intimacy = talk + time + togetherness.

Of course we learned all sorts of meaningful and honest qualities about each other's personalities over time and talk. But face-to-face contact bequeaths a wealth of observed information that is impossible to communicate any other way. So much of our language is unspoken. It is comprised of looks and gestures and sounds that are not words. Most of us don't pause to consider the vast complexity of communication unless given good reason, like I was.

I know I personally structured some of my e-mails and texts to omit and dodge certain parts of me I may not have been so proud of. Also, I was methodical in my responses, taking ample time to think about my reactions and words, which undeniably reformed them.

Don't we all play this game, though? Isn't it smart to put your best foot forward if you maintain the ability to regulate the information you share with someone? Is it not distasteful to air your dirty laundry? Hasn't social media taught us, at least to some degree, to do this more regularly and successfully? Granted, public posts are different than swapping a private e-mail with someone, yet I can't help but contemplate the fact that I'm amid a generation that's been thoroughly trained to manipulate, intentionally or not, the personal data we share electronically by editing, filtering, and creatively influencing illusions and perceptions. My generation knows exactly how to create an online persona, but that persona doesn't always tell the whole story.

But I digress, because no matter how transparent we try to be while sharing information electronically, electronic devices are only capable of transmitting less than a three dimensional figure of ourselves, less than a five sensational experience. A true and complete form of intimacy cannot be downloaded.

The devices we finger, like glowing rosaries, bring people together while paradoxically keeping them apart. As the *only* means of developing a romantic relationship, e-mails and texts and the like can never accomplish the same kind of intimacy as developed in person.

As a result, Wes and I were severely out of balance. We had a lot of talk and time under our belts but very little togetherness. Our lack of togetherness had the effect of wiping some dimension of familiarity off of us while the abundance of time and talk had the effect of intensifying a different dimension of it. The lopsided mix was tremendously confusing. And the uneven nature of our ostensibly intimate relationship was incredibly awkward when we were finally alone together.

Neither of us understood all of that, though. All we knew was that something important was off.

As we fumbled to keep conversation from waning, a series of terrible thoughts flitted across my mind. *Am I not how he remembered me? Am I not as he expected? Oh God, did he just notice the horrendous bumps on my face? Am I not as pretty as my pictures portrayed me to be?*

As we drove to the pier where his boat was docked, I tried to squash the negative thoughts crawling forth from my mental underground like zombies, spilling into my bloodstream like some sort of creepy and caustic chemical invasion. There's nothing so corrosive as fear and negativity.

I looked out the window and watched the luscious Louisiana landscape slip by as I silently recited positive affirmations, a new meditation tool I'd been practicing to combat negativity.

He squeezed my hand, and the small gesture momentarily assisted in squelching some of my fears. I looked at him. He smiled warmly. I mustered a half-smile that wasn't really a smile at all but rather some kind of placeholder.

"What?" He said. "You're so quiet."

"Are things different between us?" I blurted out without really meaning to. I meant to say something else. Something pleasant like, "Oh nothing ... I'm just enjoying this beautiful scenery. Soaking up this moment of being with you again."

He thought for a second, considering my question. "Yeah," he said but added, "that's probably normal, though." He thought for another second. "We're just gonna have to get to know each other all over again, that's all. No biggie." He shrugged his shoulders. "It'll be fine," he winked at me.

Goddamn that phrase. I shook my head. *If you didn't look so fucking cute when saying it, I'd punch you right in the throat.* I didn't say that, though. Instead of assaulting him, I found myself stifling a smirk. My face sported one of those poorly masked smiles you get when you share an inside joke with a best friend in front of someone who's not in on it.

Chapter 20

We parked and walked down the pier lined with small yachts and sailboats. Seagulls swooped overhead, screaming down at us. The water smelled strongly of algae, sort of swampy. I found myself scanning for alligators in the murky water. Wes stopped sharply and pointed out the smallest piece-of-shit-looking boat, the only hunk of crap on the strip, and said, "That one's mine."

"Oh ... " I answered back, not knowing how else to react. "That's nice," I complimented, making an effort to recover from my noticeable disappointment. I didn't want to hurt his feelings.

He laughed a wonderfully rich sound that made me want to hear it again. "That ol' thing's a piece of shit," he playfully punched my arm and shot me a wounded glance as if offended I actually believed him. He then pointed to a beautiful, pristine black-and-white yacht and said, "Welcome aboard," gesturing me to lead the way.

"Asshole," I snapped primly. I lifted my chin, disguised a smile as a line of pride, and walked away from him briskly, pretending to be a woman puffed up with importance.

He called after me, "You know, you're kinda delightful when you get all haughty like that."

I stepped aboard his yacht. As he did the same, I gave him a little push that unbalanced him. I swiftly grabbed his hand and steadied him. "Careful. I wouldn't want you fallin' in the water now." A wicked smirk danced across my face.

"Oh we're both gonna get wet, sweetheart ... and it's not gonna be because of the water." He snickered at his own wit. The insinuation quickened my pulse.

Spotless and well-maintained, his yacht sparkled in the sunlight. He gave me the grand tour. The cabin, much larger than I expected, boasted a small kitchen adjoined with a moderately sized living room, a guest and a master bedroom, and two bathrooms with full showers, all of which were immaculate and orderly. Dominated by dark and earthy colors, masculinity radiated

from the décor. I felt like I was embarking on a luxuri-
ous vacation rather than touring my boyfriend's home
for the first time.

I sensed the slight sway of the water beneath me and
heard it sloshing up against the side of the boat. It
sounded peaceful and did its part in soothing my nervous energy.

"Can I get you a drink?" He asked as he pulled a
Guinness out of the fridge for himself.

"Got anything other than beer?" I wrinkled my nose.

"Oh yeah, you're not much of a drinker are you?"

"No, not really."

"How 'bout I make you a fresh strawberry daiquiri
then? I think you'll like it." Without waiting for an answer, he pulled strawberries and a lime out of the fridge.
He rummaged around in the side cabinet for sugar, rum
and a blender before he grabbed a handful of ice from
the freezer.

With a refreshing strawberry daiquiri and a Guinness in hand, we sat on the deck of the boat watching
the sun make its leisurely descent beneath the glimmer-
ing horizon. In the low, amber light, his face looked especially striking.

Conversation, like the hot and humid Louisiana air,
felt thick and sluggish. I tried to get things rolling. "Is
it always this hot this late in the year here?"

"No, not always. Gonna be warm this week, though."

"Oh."

"Did you eat dinner yet? You hungry?"

"I'm not hungry."

"You should eat. Gotta get some meat on those bones."

"I'm not hungry," I repeated.

"Okay, suit yourself," he said.

And that's how our conversation went. It remained shallow and sort of stiff. The staleness of it waned briefly, only to return all too quickly. It wasn't half as smooth as the strawberry daiquiri I drank down.

Ever since we climbed into the car, nothing felt quite right. Nothing felt real. Everything felt different, harder than it was in the beginning. Our interaction seemed forced and tight. A weirdness sat between us. There was so much to be said after all of our time apart, yet there was really nothing that we could think to say. It appeared as though everything between us had somehow fragmented and reshaped into an entirely new form, into a configuration I scarcely recognized. We were like strangers, but even worse because we knew we shouldn't be like that.

I slurped down my second daiquiri like nobody's business, partly because of the stifling and unfamiliar humidity and partly because it was my way of executing a cowardly delay tactic while trying to think of something to fill the stubborn silence. It certainly proved to be a tasty respite from the challenge of summoning up further pleasantries. I wondered if he could actually hear the machinery of my mind grinding gears inside my skull as I tried to think of what next to say.

After my third daiquiri, I noticed the heat rising in my cheeks. The alcohol pleasantly lubricated the churning mechanisms of my mind and words seemed to glide past my lips a little easier then.

"Are you tryin' to get me drunk?" I raised one eyebrow and flashed a frisky, crooked smile his way.

"Maybe," he answered playfully.

"Well, I think it's workin'."

I moved my hand to his curly hair and used my nails to massage his scalp. He leaned into me, groaning like a dog being scratched in his sweet spot. *Maybe if we just had sex, then everything would click back into place*, I hopefully speculated.

As if his mind shared the same thought, his hand automatically started its ascent up my thigh and moved gracefully about my silky leg until just before it reached my lacy thong. Then it swept back down my leg and repeated the process several more times. Nerves and anxiety made my stomach give way as if on a scary rollercoaster ride plummeting to the earth faster than my organs could keep up.

We kissed. My face flushed. My heart tripped. My body felt like it was passing through a colossal swarm of butterflies, a million soft wings tickling and stimulating my skin all over. Every tiny hair on my body stood up, electrified. Then some noise of pleasure was out of me before I realized it had even left my mouth. As if this were his cue, he helped me out of my seat. I stood, a bit lightheaded. He led me by the hand to his bedroom.

Slowly, methodically, he removed pieces of clothing from my body, floating his hands over every morsel of skin he languidly uncovered. He unwrapped me like a brand-new, never-before-tasted box of chocolates. When the last piece of my clothing slid to the floor, he gently tossed my naked body onto his satin sheets. He masterfully undressed himself without taking his hungry eyes off of me before lowering his mass of muscles on top of my slender frame. I sank deeper in the satin sheets with the solid weight of his body atop me.

Together we felt exactly how I remembered. So why, then, did it seem like something lay between us? The emotional chemistry did not seem to match the physical. Our emotional chemistry seemed almost obligatory at the moment—like we both knew it should be there but curiously wasn't, or at least not the way it should've been. Not the way we remembered it. So we faked it. We acted. We pretended like nothing changed, as if obliged to take advantage of our full liberty, to take advantage of our togetherness.

The incredible, all-encompassing, otherworldly connection we shared before seemed faraway and small now, like something that happened in another life, or maybe in a dream.

But love like ours couldn't just be lost like that. *Could it?* I swallowed a lump of panic climbing its way up my throat, burning like acid reflux. *There's no way*, I reassured myself. Love doesn't suddenly disappear like the stairs at the end of an escalator. *Does it?*

Negative thoughts tangled in my mind like a fine silver chain. I hurried to untangle the delicate strand before it knotted beyond hope. I applied all the positive wisdom I'd been collecting over the past few months in order to keep my fears in check. I knew that once they began to put down roots and grow, they'd spread like noxious weeds. *It'll just take some time.* I reassured myself again. I thought about my faith, and in so doing, I subconsciously borrowed Wes's words. *It'll be fine.*

Unlike our previous passionate lovemaking, once he plunged inside me, there was no moment of slow sweetness. The relaxed sipping and deliberate relishing of each other that started with him leisurely peeling off my clothing ended brusquely, turning into a lustful gulping and unthinking taking. He came at me with an electric jolt of demand.

This time he moved quickly, urgently, with a crazed motion thrusting at the drum of my quickened heartbeat. Like a thoroughbred, he raced through the motions expertly. His breaths came hungrily.

It was hot and exciting and simultaneously sort of demoralizing. I didn't know it then, but I would never be rid of them, those sounds of his fervor. They would follow me, invading my future dreams.

The whole affair didn't result in an orgasm for me. Far too distracted for that, I merely held on for the ride. Besides, at that rate, he didn't last long. It'd been almost a year since either of us had gotten laid, and I could tell we were both like virgins again—me being as tight as a tick and him lasting about as long as a sneeze.

In the end, I could tell he was a little shy about the fact I didn't climax, but he played it off with a joke.

"IGM," he said. I tilted my head and furrowed my eyebrows. I had no idea what he was talking about. I thought I saw him blush ever so slightly as he explained, "IGM ... you know ... 'I got mine.'"

I bit back a smile and adopted an indignant tone. "Really? WTF ... you know ... what the fuck? How rude!" I pushed him off me in feigned disgust.

He laughed and nestled his face in his pillow. Peeking one eye out, he gave me the cutest apologetic face, like a guilty puppy trying to say he was sorry for chewing my shoes to shreds. I didn't know how he did that. How he was maddeningly sexy, impossibly cute, and totally annoying all at the same time.

I let out one of those short laughs that's more like a snort. "Gaaaaaawd. You're too cute for your own good." A smile bloomed across my face as I shook my head at him. I tousled his dark, curly locks and snuggled him. He pulled me in. We looked into each other's eyes.

I knew, right then and there that despite all the awkwardness, I was falling more in love with him. Another emotion was playing at the edges of that moment, though. A darker one whose tail I struggled to grasp. For some reason not instantly known to me, a vague unsettled sensation came over me. And then I realized why. I couldn't shake the hunch that our feelings were not mutual. I suppose it was because of the way he was looking at me right then. Or better, yet, the way he wasn't looking at me.

Before, back when we first started dating, his gaze literally caused the temperature of my skin to rise. His eyes burned with dangerous intensity. He had so much danger, so much intensity in his eyes, I couldn't look at them very long without feeling like I was about to fall off the edge of the earth. Now, his gaze fell on me softer, subdued, muted. My first thought was, irrationally, to promise him the bumps on my face would go away, that I would have my pretty skin back one day, and that I could be the beautiful woman he merited.

Wes fell asleep as a swirl of thoughts reduced me to stillness. I calmed my angst, muzzled the biting negativity, by meditating on all the things I could be grateful for. I prayed for the ability to trust God's plan.

Eventually, the gentle sway of the boat lulled me to sleep, and I slipped into slumber, feeling confident I possessed the inner strength necessary to deal with whatever came my way.

Wes woke before me and was already in the shower by the time I came to. I stole a quick scan of myself in the mirror and shuddered at the site. Smudged black eye makeup made me look like a raccoon, the bumps on my face gave me the texture of a toad, and my frazzled, humidified hair gave me the appearance of a petrified cat. I was one unfortunate looking creature.

"Fuck," I whispered under my breath.

I hustled to brush my hair and wipe off some of the wayward makeup before Wes got out of the shower. I looked at myself in the mirror again. "Fuck," I repeated. I felt like hiding my face altogether, but it was no use.

He strode out of the shower, naked, confident, and like he hadn't a worry in the world. A familiar feeling of envy slid across my chest like a slithering snake making a figure eight around my breasts. *I wish I felt that comfy in my own toad skin.*

I eagerly jumped in the shower and tried to rinse the negative residue off me. I kept the bathroom door shut as I dressed and put on my makeup, not wanting him to get a clean look at my skin ailment.

I opened one of his cabinets just to be nosy, releasing a wave of cologne that brought me back to our first date. I replayed that night in my head and wasn't sure if I had made up the ease with which we interacted back then. If that were real, then where had it gone?

We went out to breakfast at a little café near the dock, a short five-minute walk from the boat. I caught one of the young, pretty waitresses glaring at me. Wes, noticing the dirty exchange, laughed as he quietly speculated, "I think the girls are jealous of you."

At first I thought it was a nice compliment. I thought he was telling me the girls were envious because they thought I was beautiful. It took me a moment, but eventually it dawned on me that he was actually telling me the girls were jealous not because *I* was beautiful but because *he* was beautiful, because I was there with him. They were envious not because of my merit but because I was attached to the Almighty Wes. *How stupid of me*, I thought. *Of course they wouldn't be jealous of Toad Face.*

I then got the sickening sense that he had probably had sex with at least one of the waitresses working there, if not more. All of this pissed me off and poked a demon inside me, but I immediately pushed the thoughts out of my mind. Even though he was being unpardonably rude, and my scanty store of patience was beginning to run out, I was determined to focus on positivity.

I opened a fist which had clenched itself in my lap and flexed my fingers thoughtfully. I pressed them to my eyes as I recovered my equanimity. "It sure is beautiful here." I rigidly commented, trying my best to change gears.

"You shoulda seen where I was livin' in Panama. Puts this place to shame."

"Yeah, I'm sure. Aren't you glad to be home, though?" I asked.

"Yeah," he said cautiously, as if weighing his words. "For the most part." Something tickled the back of my brain as he said it. Vague words from an old e-mail. I wasn't sure.

"A part of you wishes you were still there?" I qualified.

"Yeah, kinda," he said a little hesitantly. I sensed a tenuous criticism as if he didn't approve of me asking him that question. "You have to understand, it was the best deployment of my service: great location, a lot of fishing 'n' diving, 'n' hanging out with my best buddy, Hank. It's hard to believe it's all over, you know?"

Hearing his answer opened a small hollowness within me. "Well, *I'm* glad you're home." I uttered, doing a little fishing of my own. I hoped he would say something reassuring like, "I love bein' here with you," or "The best part of bein' home is gettin' to spend time with you, my love." But all he said was, "Thank you." He seemed distracted with other thoughts.

Our conversation had a hard time taking off. It was like trying to start an old lawn mower by yanking on the pull cord until your arm is on fire. Nevertheless, I persisted in my pursuit of positivity.

"Are you looking forward to movin' back to Colorado next month?"

"Yeah, I am. It'll be good to spend some time with my family, especially my mom."

"And your girlfriend," I added, trying unsuccessfully to sound nonchalant. Though I hadn't meant it to, the end of my voice swerved up like I was asking a question, and I thought I must sound like a teenage girl, an immature, juvenile, teenage girl.

"If she's lucky," he teased. A perfect smile filled every part of his achingly handsome face. I adored how his eyes crinkled with tiny laugh lines when he smiled really big like that.

I wanted to let go. I wanted to freely slide further down the love slope and enjoy the ride while I was at it, but I couldn't. I kept digging my heels in and trying to grab on to things to slow my descent because I wasn't sure he felt the same way about me anymore.

Even if I knew he was joking about me being lucky to spend time with him, I also knew he was very skillfully playing the oh-so-casual noncommittal card. There was something different about him. I couldn't quite put my finger on it. But there was definitely something different, and it made me feel unloved.

And rightfully so. He hadn't told me he loved me since I arrived.

Chapter 21

The next three days passed, and bit by bit things started to feel a tad more comfortable. We did fun activities normal couples do like go to the movies, dine out, and take evening walks by the water. He showed me the base where he worked and introduced me to some of his coworkers/friends. We picked up pumpkins from a farmers' market and held our own carving contest. I won, though he wouldn't admit it. We also set crab traps near the boat and fished a little off the dock.

To the untrained eye we appeared perfectly normal as a couple, but I knew better. He still hadn't told me he loved me. Not once since I arrived. I didn't tell him I loved him either, though the words smoldered inside me, burning to be given voice. I wasn't sure, but I figured it might be wise to ease back into that type of intimacy. Things were obviously different between us, so I imagined it wouldn't be the right strategy to corner him into saying something he might not be ready to say.

The noticeable absence of the L word stuffed a big, fat elephant in the room everywhere we went, but what could I do? I knew if I brought attention to the elephant, I could potentially ruin our time together, or worse, be forced to face my fear of losing him. Instead, I avoided the conversational minefield, and I decided to exercise patience. I convinced myself that it would be judicious to wait until the end of my trip to bring it up. In the meantime, I strove to enjoy our time together rather than brood about things I couldn't control. It was extremely difficult.

For the last night of my stay, he made reservations at the Omni, a nice hotel in New Orleans. That day we experienced Bourbon Street and the French Quarter together. I wasn't super impressed.

In hindsight, I can now see my experience of that day was tainted due to my prophetic trepidation. Expending so much energy on restraining the strong, strangling hand of foreboding, left me uptight and in the kind of mood that's difficult to enjoy much of anything. For instance, it annoyed me that there was a Saints game that day, littering the streets with obnoxious, drunken fans.

It also irritated me that as soon as I would catch a whiff of delicious food, it would be stamped out by the nause-ating scent of sunbaked vomit and urine.

That night we feasted at a fancy restaurant, and I fi-nally had an excuse to wear the "results" dress I packed. It was a classic beauty, a red vintage piece. I always had to say a secret prayer the zipper would make it up past my wide, boney hips and then again past my breasts, but it gave me the outline of a 1950s starlet. It's just one of those dresses you can't help but feel good in, you know? It was as tight and fitted as a second layer of skin and showed off all the right places. The deep red satin fabric brought out the blue in my eyes and the natural auburn lowlights in my glossy golden hair. It would've looked like I walked right off one of those pinup posters except for the loathsome bumps on my face.

"Well don't you look pretty," Wes said when I emerged from the bathroom.

"Thank you," I replied, still finding it impossible to feel completely confident in myself, considering the state of my skin.

"That's a grab-you-by-the-balls-sexy kind of dress," he persisted, kindly offering to fluff my visibly droopy feathers.

I politely returned his praise. "You look very hand-some yourself."

"Thank you. Had this suit tailored in Colombia. Fits me to a T," he said breezily.

"I'll say," I agreed. The perfectly sized suit and white button-down shirt complemented his dark good looks effortlessly. I quietly hated him for what little time he had to put forth in order to look nothing short of phenomenal.

We walked hand in hand to the restaurant, only a block from our hotel. His hand in mine felt like the most natural thing in the world.

He ordered us oysters and extravagant drinks. I opened my mouth to say something nice about the food and instead said suddenly, "Wes, do you feel the same way about me?"

The words dropped from my mouth like pebbles. I had no idea where they came from. I didn't mean to ask him that, not right then. I meant to give it more time. He needed more time. Or maybe I did. I wasn't ready for his answer.

He didn't reply right away. I watched his face, searching from something in his eyes and his expression. Silence settled over our table like ash. I breathed deep to dispel the panic, but my fears began to spread like creeping spider veins. He looked at me compassionately, and the sadness in his eyes gave away his answer before he even spoke. I forced myself not to look away. Nor did I tap my foot nervously on the floor or scratch the itch making its hot and uncomfortable way across my neck. I held his gaze. I begged him with my eyes not to break my heart.

"I don't think so, Mila," he finally replied.

His words ricocheted between my ears, screaming like stray bullets. I flinched at the sting of it. A pain slashed at my heart as savagely as a wild animal's fangs. He shook and bowed his head, unable to look any longer at my pained expression. And the question nibbling at the corners of my brain finally dropped its question mark.

I took a deep breath and closed my eyes, heavy with grief. I kept them closed, too, as if the secret to the way back to his heart might be inscribed on the insides of my lids.

"I'm sorry, Mila. I really am." He struggled for the right words. I muscled my laden eyelids open so I could meet his eyes again. They were dark and unreadable. He wiped his hand across his whole face as if trying to erase his features.

I held him there with a still, steady gaze, forcing him to speak again. He stumbled through his explanation. "I'm ... um ... going through some ... uh ... big changes right now, and ... um ... it might take some time for the dust to settle."

What a load of crap! I almost yelled it at him. I stopped just short of it. I inhaled deeply, and let the breath leave me slowly. I wrestled my thoughts, trying to form a response that might seem a little less brash.

"Big changes?" I repeated his words. They came out choppy like traversing ocean waves in a small boat on a windy day. Sarcasm saturated my tone so thoroughly that he knew my emotions threatened to boil over. "Big changes." I said it again, more to myself this time than to him, as if tasting the words. I curled my lips into something that resembled a smile. "How terrible for you," I said in a voice as sweet and bitter as burned caramel.

Silence, again, descended over us like gun powder, primed and ready to explode with the slightest touch of a match. Tension, as swift and sharp as the Benchmade in his front right pocket, sliced the room in half. For the small space between us, we were divided into entirely different realities, no longer united in the slightest. I stared at my half of the table, trying to quell the rising sense of fury bubbling up to my throat from the pit of my belly. My eyes glittered with barely suppressed rage. The pressure rising in my chest sprouted tentacles and squeezed my lungs, pushing acrimonious words up my esophagus and out my mouth.

"There was a time not too long ago, if you kindly recall, that I also went through a lot of 'big changes,'" I said. My voice quivered with criticism. Every time I repeated the phrase "big changes" my hands mockingly formed air quotes, no doubt underscoring my attempt at hurling his words back at him like tiny little daggers. "None of those 'big changes' changed the way I felt about you, though." Disappointment and a deep, penetrating accusation dripped like blood from my words.

"But you did break up with me," he said, a barb of defensiveness in his response. It looked like he was about to say something more, but the barely controlled rage on my face must have snapped his throat shut.

"You're gonna throw that at me now?" I all but foamed from the mouth as my fulminating glare fizzed and crackled like a rabid dog. "I thought we were past that. I've grown so much since then. I've improved. You haven't even given me a real chance!" I spat the words at him.

"I don't know what you want me to say, Mila. I don't feel that same way I once did about you." He spoke calmly and left no room for debate. I saw heartbreak in his shoulders but relief in his eyes. Confusion contorted my face. I tried to swallow, but it felt like there were broken pieces of my heart caught in my throat, obstructing the way.

He paused, picking his words carefully, before very directly and simply stating, "Mila ... I'm not in love with you anymore." The words rifled out of his mouth and lodged themselves deep in me, so deep they cut through my very soul. Even though I wondered if everything in the past few days was leading to this, even though it was a fear I repeatedly entertained from the first day I fell in love with him, still, the moment ripped through me. My body seemed to give a tremendous jolt, as if I just missed my first step on the stairs. My belly clutched as the room violently tilted, and I felt that any moment I would slide off the edge of the earth.

My mouth suddenly felt papery. I had never endured such rejection before. I didn't know what to say.

Wes said nothing more, sensing my volatile state. I closed my eyes, on the verge of tears. Every cell in my body shivered as if frostbitten. I was living in my own private winter. But when I looked down at my hands, they oddly lay calm and quiet in my lap. I suppose shock momentarily paralyzed my body.

After a long minute of agonizing silence, Wes picked up his fork and began eating. I scowled at him as I thought: *How? How can you eat at a time like this? You don't care at all, do you? You're a fucking monster!*

Rage hit me so hard I saw spots before my eyes. I knowingly stoked the fire of my anger, too, feeding it tidbits about his heartless, calloused behavior, because I think I subconsciously realized that just beyond the rage was a sorrow so enervating it could render me immobile.

With fire in my eyes and steel in my back, I briskly stood ramrod straight. I needed to leave. I needed to leave before the rage gave way and mugged me of my ability to walk.

"Mila, please sit down and eat your dinner." He sat there completely relaxed in his chair as if poured there.

"I'm not hungry," I seethed at him.

"You need to eat."

"Why? 'Cause I'm too fuckin' skinny?" I flung my words at him like an angry monkey throws its own shit. My throat felt raw, like a wound. "Am I not pretty enough for you?" I asked with a look and tone that could make any man's balls shrink to the size of marbles.

"Mila ... " he said deliberately, sounding like someone forced to explain something politely to an imbecile. He put his hand on my arm, and I forced myself not to jerk it away. "Listen," he started, wagging his fork at me with the air of a wise man delivering an aphorism, "I know you're angry and hurt right now. But you'll see this is for the best. Everything'll work out." He kept his voice easy. He paused before he amiably added, "It'll be fine."

His cool nature and "it'll be fine" attitude caused an intense and overwhelming burning sting just between my collarbones. His stupid platitudes intended to comfort me made me want to push him off his high horse. He might have struck a match to kerosene my temper flared so hot.

I leaned close to him, my stare falling on him as hard and cold as winter metal. I leaned so close that our faces were only inches apart, lending emphasis to what I was about to say. My voice dropped to a husky tenor, thick with emotion. I hissed in the meanest most venomous way I could, "Fuck you, Wes. I hate you." My face moved closer to his, our mouths so close we could have accidentally kissed. "I *hate* you," I said again, stressing the

words by using the powerful breath from my lower ab-
domen. He winced then. And I think if he had been a
turtle, he would've retreated into his shell.

I took a nasty pleasure in that, but I didn't stop there.
My pain was a nest of furious cicada killer wasps, while
the pain I inflicted on him was probably nothing but a
tiny anthill in comparison. So I tried to hurt him more.

"You're a horrible human being, Wesley Blackwell.
You're so selfish ... heartless. A goddamned monster!
You don't feel anything, do you?" I almost stopped there
but surged on. "I don't know what the fuck you did with
your heart, but it's not inside you anymore. I hope you
rot in hell for the way you use women up and then dump
them like trash. You don't deserve love. You're incapable of it!"

I realized almost as soon as I said it—upon hearing
the hatred in my words and seeing how they twisted and
regrouped in the air into something abusive and vilify-
ing—I knew already how I would've felt if he had said
the same to me. My sick outburst made me feel like I had
just retched, violently. I stood up straight, wiping the
back of my hand across my trembling lips.

I felt tears coming but held them back. I didn't want
to cry in front of him, but the pain in damming my tears
made it hard to breathe. I feared I couldn't stop the torrent any longer. I sensed my willpower tearing from its
moorings, tears sizzling through my temper.

I turned on my heel and ran out of the restaurant without a backward glance. He didn't stand a chance to say a single word before I vanished. When I really wanted to, I could move like a whippet with the kind of swiftness not even a rabbit could outmaneuver.

Once I hit the street, I walked quickly but extra carefully as I tried to stabilize the ground tipping beneath my feet. I hated that I looked something like all the other drunks littering the sidewalks as I struggled to secure the pavement that failed me.

Crying was a weakness I detested, an activity I strove never to indulge in, especially in front of a man who was breaking my heart. It required every microscopic element of my energy to hold back until I reached the privacy of our hotel room. I slid my key in the door, heard the beep that signified access, and then, just like that, my heart was given permission to shatter into a bazillion sharp and cutting pieces like an explosion of a glass skyscraper.

My face crumpled. My composure decayed. I hardly made it to the couch before my knees buckled, spilling me to the cushions. I collapsed to the couch like a burning piece of paper. I shriveled up there like a shrunken, wrinkled balloon. Using a pillow, I muffled my irrepressible sobbing. A dam, too long in the making, broke, and I felt utterly hopeless in the onslaught. It overcame me and tore at my heart and my gut and my soul, and it brutally pulled me under, and I couldn't bear it. I honest to God thought I couldn't bear it.

The blood beat so hard in my head it hurt. The internal roar of agony grew so loud I feared it might strip the membranes in my ears. I didn't know for sure if it was heartbreak that was causing me to fiercely tremble or if, perhaps, the earth was literally quaking and crumbling beneath me. In the case of the latter, I hoped the ground would do me a favor and swallow me whole into its darkness and nothingness.

I heard Wes enter the room, but I barely lifted my face from the pillow. Unable to stop my sorrow from spilling out of me, my wailing continued. I could tell by the way his whole body cringed that the horrifying, guttural noises of agony spewing forth from my mouth penetrated his skin like tiny needles.

I despised him seeing me like that. It appalled me to feel the angry tears spilling hot down cheeks, to hear the torture in my outcry. I was completely undone, totally unhinged, an embarrassing emotional wreck. I wanted to disappear.

He didn't know what to do. He raked his fingers through his perfect hair and stood at the door considering if he should leave me alone to cry it out. But he stayed.

He said my name, trying to sooth me. "Mila." When I didn't look up at him, he said it again. "Mila." Every time he said my name, he made it worse. The sound of my name on his lips—the lips I kissed, the lips that tasted like my future, my forever—the sound of my name on his lips was the most tragic music I had ever heard. It was a beautiful, operatic melody summoning the deepest, most dramatic sense of loss of my life.

The third time he said it, I paused. I heaved my heavy head from the pillow and looked at him. When our eyes met he almost immediately looked away, and I knew then there must've been a haunting look of despair about me that went straight to his heart. And I think it made him gentler with me than he had likely ever been with any person in all the world.

I buried my head back into the pillow, crying, but much softer this time. He kneeled on the floor next to the couch and placed a hand on my shuddering back, saying nothing. He rested his forehead on the edge of the couch near my face, and I thought for an instant he might also be crying.

His compassion actually made the misery of it worse. It reminded me of everything I lost. It retold everything I fought for but never won. It recapped my sad saga of how a lifelong companionship, kind of like the unexpected rainbow in the spray of a water hose, disappeared only moments after I spied a beautiful glimpse of it. Nothing but a mirage.

Between sniffles I told him to leave me alone, my voice catching in my throat. I hated the sound of it. The sound of my own weakness. But he refused. He easily hacked past the lazy passwords of my defenses. He lured my limbs off the couch into his arms on the floor and pleaded with me to stop crying.

I couldn't look away from his gaze. His eyes were hypnotizing. Compassion radiated from them. I was angry at him—I knew that, I felt it deep in my core—but as he cradled me against his body, that anger burned up and blew away like ashes, only a shallow sentiment lightly blanketing a longing that mattered so much more. I rested my head on his chest, and he tilted toward me so that his head rested on top of mine.

As he held me, I did something I had never done after a breakup, never even imagined I was capable of after such blatant rejection.

I kissed him.

I kissed him, hoping to bring him back to me. I thought maybe it wasn't too late, not yet anyway. I kissed him and let my lips linger there so that our breath mingled and eventually married into a single scent. I pressed my face against his so that tears from my eyes became brine on his skin. I kissed him and held him. And I wished, I hoped, I prayed he'd come back to me.

He kissed me back. It was a sad kiss, an act of contrition. A kiss that overflowed with tenderness and grace. A kiss loaded with emotion, smothered in unfulfilled yearning, and topped with deep disappointment. Disappointment, not in me, but in his own emotions which could not be helped. His eyes tattled on him. His lips did, too. Our kiss was so intimate that I knew—I could taste—his desire to change his own heart. But he couldn't. It was out of his hands.

Yet I was in his hands. And the moment, rich in affection and communion, led his hands to pull me even closer to his chest. He folded me into him. He embraced me like he might embrace a dying soldier, and I thought: *How? How in the world can you tell me you don't love me anymore?* There was so much love in his hands. In his eyes. His lips.

I wanted to show him the way back to his love for me. I kissed his mouth, his face, his neck. I kissed my own tears from his skin. I touched my hand to his heart and said a silent prayer that the love in my hand would act like a magnet and draw forth the love I knew he had hidden somewhere.

And then, following some unstoppable urge, I made love to him. I hoped that tiny, invisible parts of him would become tiny, invisible parts of me. I made love to him. Like a sponge, I tried to absorb him. I tried to make him forever a part of me. I wanted to imprint every bit of him on myself. I pressed every bit of me against him. I gave him every bit of love I had.

I fought for him. I fought harder for Wesley than any person ever before. I had to. I know it seems crazy, but I knew that in spite of everything that had happened, he was my soul mate. I had never loved anyone quite the way I loved him: beyond reason.

People think a soul mate is your perfect match, the person who completes you and complements you, the person who miraculously fills all the gaps in your heart and your life. And that's what everyone wants. But like Elizabeth Gilbert wisely pointed out, "A true soul mate is a mirror, the person who shows you everything that is holding you back, the person who brings you to your own attention so you can change your life."

Wes was the living reflector who helped me change my own life. He helped me see further inside myself. He brought me closer to my own attention. He didn't complete me; he helped me understand how I might complete myself. Because of him, I would never be the same.

Our relationship hummed a holy tune in my soul. He stirred something within me that helped me find my path back to a better place. He revealed to me a corner of my heart that life had shut down. He inspired me to go after a bigger and fuller existence than I ever gave myself credit for, and I was immensely thankful to him for that. He touched my soul like it had never been touched before. Nothing could make me stop loving him. Not even him telling me he didn't love me anymore.

And when you love someone, truly love someone, you set him free.

I made love to him one last time with unreserved sincerity and passion. This was startling in its intimacy, stripped of any pretense. It was the most powerful and beautiful, while synchronously heartbreaking and tragic love I'd ever made. I handed him my entire being and he handed me his, and through touch alone, we said our best and final farewell.

Early in the morning, I packed my bags without bothering to fold my clothes. I started to call a cab to pick me up from the hotel, but Wes insisted on driving me to the airport. We drove in thirty minutes of muteness. Sadness stretched between us as taut as the surface of a bubble, ready to be popped.

The passing scenery moved in and out of focus, like my thoughts. I drove hundreds of questions away from my tongue. I wanted an explanation. I needed one. Yet I resigned myself to letting him go without any more of a fuss.

I sought to set him free.

Do you know how hard it is to say nothing when every part of you strains to say something? I wanted to say something that might change his mind. I wanted him to say something that might help me understand. But neither of us said anything.

When we arrived at the airport, Wes lifted my bags from the trunk and put them on the ground near me. He pulled me into his arms for a goodbye hug.

"I'm gonna miss you." I said in a voice so brittle it sounded like it might snap.

He frowned and murmured, "I'll miss you too." A quiver had crept into his words, and they came out muffled, like his esophagus was too tight, and they could barely squeeze through.

He dared to say it again. "It'll be fine, Mila."

I nodded, but even as I moved my head in agreement, I thought: *How? For the love of God, how?! How will I walk away and leave you now?*

"Yeah sure," I said with a shrug, though my eyes said otherwise.

If there was one thing I learned for certain on that trip, it was that I wanted him. I wanted his companionship, his love, his presence in my life. I wanted him more than I wanted my next breath. And the expression in his remorseful eyes revealed to me that he understood, now, for the first time, what I had been afraid of from the very beginning.

By some small miracle, I lifted my chin, head held high with the façade of pride, and walked away from him. I walked straight to the restroom, not evening taking the time to check-in for my flight. I stared at myself in the mirror trying to talk myself down from another emotional episode. All I could see looking back at me were the bumps on my face.

I learned something else for certain. I learned that loss was not only probable but unavoidable ... that it must be my lot in life to be taught this lesson time and time again.

Unable to look at the bumps in the mirror any longer, I locked myself in a stall and put my head between my hands. I sat there until the fire in my chest eased to smoldering embers. To cry then and there was an indulgence I refused to grant myself. I had always respected people who stayed strong, especially when they had every right to break down. *Today*, I thought, *I will be one of those people.*

Eventually, I checked in and made my way to the terminal. When I got there, I found a semi-private place and called my mom.

"Hey Ma," I said sullenly when she answered the phone.

"Hey, what's wrong? You sound so sad."

"He doesn't love me anymore, Mom." Tears pricked my eyes like little porcupine quills as I retold the story of what happened.

"Oh Mila. I'm so sorry." Her voice expressed as much pain as my own. I knew she was grieving with me.

"I don't know what I did wrong." I choked.

"Babe, you didn't do anything wrong. Life is just like that sometimes." She paused for a beat. "Sometimes life can be just like the tiny white puff on the top of a dandelion. Just one wisp and ... poof ... it can be scattered across the atmosphere. Just like that. Sometimes it's amazing. Sometimes it's not. You didn't do anything wrong."

"Ma," I vacillated briefly as I lassoed the courage to continue. "Do you think he stopped loving me because of the awful bumps on my face? I feel so hideous."

"For heaven's sake child, no! You're gorgeous!" I could hear the tears in her voice now. "Do you know how many women would kill to look like you? You can barely see those damn bumps anyway. And if that is the reason, then good riddance to bad rubbish! You don't want a man who's so vain he would leave you because of a passing skin ailment."

She was right. I knew she was right. So why, then, was it so hard for me to convince myself? Why was it so hard for me to love myself? The loud, mean voice in my head fed me lies. It told me I was ugly. I was unworthy. That there was something seriously wrong with me.

"Thanks mom," I said softly. We ended our conversation. I could tell by the pull in her voice she had a hard time hanging up. She wanted to take my pain away.

Before I boarded the plane, everyone in my immediate family knew about the breakup. It's one of the good and bad things about a tight-knit family. My sister-in-law Lucy called me right away.

"What the fuck is wrong with him? I'll chop his fucking balls off! I swear, Mila, I'll do it." She took a long breath and stopped talking until the boil in her chest dropped to a simmer. "I'm so sorry, honey. I just can't stand to hear such misery in your voice. I'd do anything for you. You know that, right?"

By the time I talked to the last person in my family, I could no longer keep my body from sagging. Emotionally drained, I sobbed, bent doubled over, a curtain of golden silk sheltering my face.

It was under that curtain I said a simple prayer. I didn't really want to say it. In fact, I felt a little like one of those children being forced by a parent to apologize for something I did not feel sorry for. It may not have been the sincerest of prayers, but it was the right thing to do, so I tried to do it. Truly, I tried my best to be genuine, despite the anger swelling inside me. *Papa, I'm angry and disappointed. I'm heartbroken and feeling lost. But I am willing to see this situation differently. Please heal my perspective. Change my heart and my thoughts. Guide me back to inner peace.*

Chapter 22

The thing about spiritual growth few people will tell you is that it is like a detoxification of your soul. All the bad stuff has to surface in order to be released. And like Pema Chödrön said, "Nothing ever goes away until it has taught you what you need to know." Many lessons, admittedly and regrettably, have to be learned much more than once in a lifetime. I should know.

I was unprepared for this detoxification process. Before I went out to see Wes, I was pretty damn confident I had finally figured things out. I held the secret. I cracked the code. Fit with spiritual muscles, I was finally ready for a healthy relationship.

The depth of torment I suffered as a result of losing my soul mate came as a big surprise to me. It bitch-slapped me, hard. It popped my kneecaps out from under me. I thought I spiritually equipped myself for all possible outcomes. But I hadn't. And what's more, I failed. I failed to manifest my dreams. Like the good student I am, I had fastidiously practiced and applied all the techniques I studied in order to be in a place conducive to fostering a healthy relationship. I would've bet my bottom dollar that I had aced the course. But I failed. I left empty-handed.

Beyond that, and more importantly, I thought I had primed myself for finding joy in my relationship with God alone, that I no longer depended on another to give me the gift of joy. But I was proven wrong.

In the shock of it all, I began questioning the validity of my newfound wisdom. My inner spires of faith and hope started collapsing as an internal earthquake of doubt compromised the integrity of all of the new beautiful and divine architecture I painstakingly constructed on the property of my soul.

I started wondering if I had what it took. I wondered where God was in all of this. I questioned why He never seemed to answer my heartfelt prayers, my deepest desires. And then I wondered what the point in praying was. I speculated that perhaps I'd be better off if I stopped desiring the good things natural to my soul. It had been my experience that those things were kind of like cotton candy: they disappeared the second I got a taste of their sweetness.

I was hanging onto a ledge, high above the blackness. Dark thoughts I had quarantined to the furthest closet in my mind, thoughts I had buried beneath one of the floor boards, unearthed themselves and pounced on my faith. I dug my fingernails into the earth of the ledge, holding on with all my might. I dangled there, suspended, for as long as my skinny arms could hold me. But in the pain and grief of it all, I just couldn't hold on anymore.

I fell.

I gave myself over to the darkness.

I sank to a cold, dark place where no light could reach me. Winter crusted my soul with a hard, icy distrust and disbelief. For the next few weeks I became thoroughly unreachable, completely absorbed in my own anguish. I lost myself again. There is no language for the loss I grieved inside me, the profundity of my pain too deep and expansive to express in words. I barely ate. I hardly bathed. I was past hunger, past vanity, past caring. I mourned not only the loss of the man I'd thought was my soul mate, but even greater, the loss of my inner peace, the loss of my faith, the desertion of something precious I had just found.

Birdie texted me asking how my trip out to Louisiana went. Apparently Wes had not told her he broke up with me. I had to break the news to her. She was shocked and sad for us. She said, "That doesn't make any sense. I saw with my own eyes how much he loved you ... but, if that boy can't see what he's got, then he doesn't deserve to have it. I hope you and I will continue to talk. I really enjoy having you as my friend."

As challenging as it was at times, I did continue to talk to Birdie. I didn't believe in building relationships based solely on a relationship with someone else, so the end of my relationship with Wes did not affect my relationship with Birdie. It was hard, and it was cathartic at the same time. Every time I talked to her I was reminded of him, but she helped me through some of my pain. She supported and loved me, and that was exactly what I needed at the time.

My whole family supported me, too. I received visits, phone calls, texts, and e-mails from my siblings. My parents went out of their way to show me their love. They treated me with kid gloves. My dad would come home from the grocery store with my favorite snacks. My mom would prepare my favorite meals. I couldn't eat much, though. I appreciated their kindness, but I just wanted to be left alone to mourn in solitude. I didn't have the energy to form sentences for conversation or to do much of anything other than lie around and sulk.

It wasn't fair, you know. The breakup wasn't. True, over the course of our relationship I was a little all over the place. That much was for sure. But I loved him, and there was no doubting that. And if you knew me at all, you knew that when I loved someone or something, I loved really big. And if I loved you, you knew it. I made damn sure of it.

Maybe I loved a little too big, was a little too dramatic, a little too dependent, but I didn't deserve that. I could have matured, I think, if he had given me a chance. He didn't give me a proper chance. He didn't give us a suitable opportunity to settle back into our relationship after his deployment.

He just threw us away. How could he do that? It wasn't fair. And, yes, I know: life's not fair. But at that time, all I wanted to do was sulk about it.

So I started smoking marijuana incessantly again. The first time I took a hit, it was all I could do to keep myself from moaning with lustful pleasure as the drug lapped all my sensory receptors with its miniature THC tongues. With each hit, I expected everything to change. I anticipated the crumbling of the white-hot rock of anger and sorrow that sat inside me. But nothing happened. I still felt it there, a lump of concrete, scraping me bloody and sore from the inside out.

I labored to ingest so much marijuana that the drug might fill my head with Elmer's Glue. I aimed to gum-up my inner workings so thoroughly that I might stop dissecting my last visit with him. That I might stop analyzing what I had missed that I should've seen. That I might stop replaying each moment, searching for what

I might've done differently to change everything. That I might stop picking it down to the bones, wondering how it had all gone so miserably wrong.

I must've replayed the tragic trip a gazillion times in the theater of my mind. It was a running loop of misery. I ruminated and brooded over every tiny detail. I thought and thought until I thought my brain might bleed from the effort.

Interestingly enough, time contracts and lengthens. It's not weighted evenly like the clock on the wall suggests. Certain moments remain in the mind while others disappear. This, no doubt, was one of those moments that expanded and claimed an unfair portion of my memory drive. I attempted to move it where it belonged: the recycling bin. I wanted it to evaporate and blow away into never-never land. So I smoked. I smoked until I convinced myself I just might successfully banish the details caught in the crevices of my memory.

All the little details. The strong scent of Hoppe's No. 9 gun cleaner on his hands. The smell of his neck—clean and sharp, like the air after a rainstorm. The twitching in his sleep that would wake us both with a start. The dirty and wildly inappropriate lyrics he made up while attempting to sing along (horribly off-key) with songs on the radio. The crookedness of his right pinky finger. The tattoo of Poseidon's trident on his left calf. The way he always chose his seat so his back was never to the door. The random bobby pins in his shoes and clothing "just in case" he needed to pick a lock. The sound of his low, rich laugh. The flash of his arrestingly handsome smile. The turbulence in his lusty-for-life eyes. All the little details.

I tried to smoke them out, but it was like nailing jelly to the wall. It was like trying to wipe up the ocean with a single paper towel. No amount of marijuana could erase him from my memory. He had become a permanent part of me. It was as though he had settled into my DNA, and I could no more easily forget his details than forget my own name. At one point, I thought that was what I wanted, for him to be a perpetual part of me. But now that I had it, I balked at my own naïveté.

In reality, the smoking did nothing except make me feel like I was underwater. It made everything move in slow motion. It only served to magnify and garble the details. I felt sort of compressed and submarine, as if I had been submerged in a murky aquarium overfull of fishy memories. Yet I kept smoking, hoping I might drown in the water.

And in some ways I did. I consumed marijuana to the point I utterly abandoned myself to slumber. Sometimes—except for the couple of miserable days each week that I had to drag myself to work—I slept all day. On the days I was left to mope in my bed, practically nothing could make me rise. Noises flitted about the house—my mom cooking breakfast for my dad, a dog barking, the washing machine cycling, a door opening

and closing, my mom poking her head in my room saying my name. No matter the noise, I slept. I inhabited
sleep firmly. I willed it. I wielded it. Sleep became my
opiate. My oblivion.

Sometimes sleep dared to desert me. But I pretended. I made my eyes still under my eyelids. I made my
mind quiet and slow. I thought about things that molli-
fied me. I imagined Wes apologizing to me. I thought
about him calling me and asking for my forgiveness,
asking if we could start over somehow. I imagined us
making up, him kissing me, his hands on my waist. The
thoughts, even though I knew they were imaginary, released pressure in my chest like someone letting air out
of a balloon. I daydreamed like that until sleep, as if recognizing a perfect reproduction of itself, eventually
came back to me.

Chapter 23

One morning roughly a week after returning home, I caught sight of my face in the bathroom mirror. I'd been avoiding mirrors since all I could see were the ugly bumps on my face, but that day I accidentally caught sight of myself.

My face appeared uninhabited, vacant. I looked paper-skinned, emaciated, sallow. I had dark circles around my eyes and tangled hair. I looked dead. Completely gutted with grief. No wonder everyone was so worried about me.

I had never been so far removed from reality. And after a couple full weeks of it, I started clawing my way back out of the darkness as best I could. I knew I couldn't live like that forever. Not in my parents' basement, anyway. That shit would not fly much longer.

Besides, I was starting to feel something like a fraud. It's not like I lost a child or the husband I'd been married to for over a decade or someone in my family. When it came down to it, I barely knew Wes, and there wasn't anything I could do to change what happened between us. There was nothing left for me to do but lick my wounds and limp about the world. There was nowhere else for me to go but on.

Plus, I presumed that actually getting up had to be marginally preferable to living in my bed batting away the flapping fucked-up-ness of my thoughts. At first, I moved about the world like a mummy. Any kind of movement was a huge undertaking, like dragging my own body against its will, like dragging the weight of the world behind me. Everywhere I went I slumped so far over I looked like a question mark missing its lower dot. Conversations washed over me, slipped around me, snagged now and then when I was expected to react somehow.

I was a dead man walking. I wanted to pray, but my faith felt far away as if it were the remnant of another woman's life.

Not able to rely on my spirituality anymore, I attempted to pull all my old tricks out of the hat. I obviously started with marijuana, then excessive sleep, and in due course, I turned to my favorite: vanity. I focused on clearing my skin ailment. I spent more on skin products than the GDP of a small African country. If someone would've told me that smearing elephant pee on my face would've cured the problem, I would've snuck into the Denver Zoo and taken a long, steamy bath in it.

Nothing made the bumps disappear or even fade. I got to the point where I tortured myself hundreds of times a day by looking in the mirror endlessly and scrutinizing how revolting they were. So, naturally, I bought more expensive makeup and new, sexy clothing. I whitened my teeth. I started working out like a possessed person. I restricted my diet even further. I did everything in my power to improve my beauty in order to compensate for the insidious bumps.

I asked Lucy to take pictures of me and, of course, edit out my bumps. The photos turned out remarkably, mostly because my sister-in-law works magic behind the lens. She knows the perfect lighting and most generous angles. I posted the photos on Facebook, seeking validation from others about my worth and beauty. A part of me hoped Wes would see the photos and realize what a horrible mistake he had made. The other more sensible side of me realized that the photos merely fostered an illusion, and if Wes did try to reach out to me, he'd be dissatisfied to learn the bumps still blemished my face.

When vanity failed to salve my wounded heart, I started dating again, desperate for a solid distraction and for some kind of concrete proof that I was still beautiful and lovable. I wasn't looking for anything serious. That had eluded me for so long I now considered the desire for it as self-destructive. I wanted a simple distraction. No strings attached.

Perhaps what I really wanted was to give a real go at this whole having-sex-just-for-fun thing that so many people seemed to successfully accomplish. Don't get me wrong—I wasn't looking to become one of those girls who receives more loads than a community washing machine, but I thought maybe I could enjoy a random casual exchange of pleasure with an agreeable stranger. Maybe there would be less pain involved in that kind of casual lifestyle.

With this mindset, it wasn't long before I allowed myself to be sweet-talked by a bar rat on the hunt, with eyes of kind consideration and masculine hands with a touch that lingered. Deep down I knew better, but alcohol impaired my judgement (like I meant for it to ... like I needed it to), and the daily weight of my miserable existence deadened the warnings. That night, my clothes fell in a small, reproving pile on the floor beside me. Contrary to the physical deed, it all felt empty. Meaningless.

Afterwards, I instantly felt grimy, as if I were soiled with filth and muck. I left as soon as the deed was done and turned the shower on hot when I got home. So hot I couldn't stand still beneath it. I had to keep turning, like something on a spit, offering the scalding water a new patch of flesh with each rotation. I looked like a red lobster by the time I scoured the imaginary grime from my skin.

Nope. Now I knew I was definitely not a having-sex-just-for-fun kind of girl. Absolutely not that kind of girl. The things I love about sex the most are the intimacy, the sharing of love, the emotional and spiritual communion. Without these things, sex isn't all that appealing to me I found out. Maybe I'm different like that. Or maybe other people are just better at lying to themselves. I don't know.

In the end, I grew mighty tired of doing nothing but flinging shit at the wall, seeing what might stick. None of the shit I flung ever stuck very long. So several months after the breakup, after all of my old tricks only temporarily brought me relief but ultimately tugged me down deeper into my own twisted wretchedness, yet again, I finally surrendered to my very last scrap of hope.

I said a prayer.

I hadn't allowed myself to do that, not with any real sincerity anyway, since before I left Louisiana. The thought of praying made me angry, and the anger festered the wounds inside me, further infecting me with depression. But I had nowhere else to turn. No more tricks up my sleeve. No more energy to keep up my ridiculous charade.

With tears sliding through my lashes, I beseeched, *Papa, I don't want to give up on You, but I'm giving up on me.*

It was a trifling and pathetic prayer, but it was all I could manage. I remember the incident like it happened yesterday. I was in my room, folded over my bed on my knees. My head down in my velvety red comforter, my body limp with depression. My soul scrubbed raw with a steel-wire brush.

A miracle took place that day.

God answered my prayer on the spot. He opened a secret valve in my soul and love and forgiveness and peace poured inside me. I experienced a healing phenomenon only the Holy Spirit is capable of. There exists no accurate or comprehensive way to explain it. There is no logic to it. No science behind it. All I know now and all I knew then is that, miraculously, I felt healed. It wasn't a physical healing, which is what I thought I wanted. But it was a spiritual healing, which is what I actually needed.

When that secret valve opened in my soul, all the love and forgiveness pouring inside me restored my inner peace. My body felt light as if floating in a pool of warm water. God's love washed over me, and I felt cleaner somehow. I felt lighter, brighter, stronger, encouraged, and most importantly, I felt lovable again.

I suddenly didn't care so much about the stupid bumps on my face. I forgave Wes for not loving me. I forgave myself for doing the same. I gave God my weakness, and, in return, He gave me His strength.

I cried then. Not weeping, but a silent, gentle cry. A cleansing of something leaving me. Many things, in fact. Anger. Anxiety. Angst. Animosity. A lot. A whole alphabet of alliteration I hadn't yet found words for. For the first time since the breakup, my worries and heartbreak were gone. My hatred transformed.

I took a sigh of deep relief, like that of the desert walker finally delivered to water. It felt as though a headache I had not really known I had lifted all at once. A lightness filled my chest as if a great breath of cool mountain air filled me.

I experienced a joy so strong it swept away all the bad stuff. If even only fleeting, it was a miracle. A moment of pure love I will never forget and for which I will always be grateful. In that moment, I could see for the first time in months that the sun was still shining behind the clouds.

It was that day, in that instant, through that miracle, I decided that instead of getting bitter, I would get better. Instead of leaving myself to rot in the past, I would join my present and choose to become someone I could be proud of. I chose to draw nearer to God and allow Him to purify me because I knew now I could not do it without Him.

I entered the most holy of all places that day. As the incredibly wise Helen Shucman said, "The holiest of all spots on earth is where an ancient hatred has become a present love." All of my pain, hatred, and negativity transformed into love and forgiveness.

And, strangely, once again, my breakdown led to my breakthrough. Although now, in retrospect, I guess it really wasn't that strange after all. I've come to understand that when pain is the greatest, it is actually a hidden opportunity for spiritual growth. I know that sounds sort of awful, but it's true, and it's actually more encouraging than awful.

It's easy to display faith when times are good. Real faith, though, shows up in our darkest hours. Think about it. The devil would prefer we not go into crisis. The devil prefers that a mild river of despair run through the background of our lives, never quite bad enough to make us question whether our own choices are feeding the flow of our pain. Never bad enough so that we might spiritually surrender to something deeper and more meaningful than the temporal world around us. Never bad enough to make us reach for something bigger than ourselves.

Like I've said before, that's the thing about misery. Once we're in it, we'll do just about anything to find a way out. Sometimes the way out is healthy. Other times it's not. Obviously, I've known both responses. One is a quick fix that treats the symptoms while the other is a long-term remedy that heals the problem. Negativity, I learned, is like a parasite, it cannot survive without a willing host. It *can* be cured. That's why I made a declaration that day to get better. I vowed to walk fully in faith and to discard my crutches of fear.

I once again approached it one step at a time. Sounds laborious, right? But, unfortunately, I knew it was the only way. First, I revisited the book *Man's Search for Meaning*, by Dr. Viktor Frankl. The book opens with a quote from Nietzsche: "He who has a why to live for can bear almost any how." It is the essence of what Dr. Frankl taught. He called it logotherapy. He said, "You must teach people to find meaning in their suffering, and in so doing they will be able to turn their personal tragedies into personal triumphs ... if [they] cannot find meaning, they will ultimately perish."

And so I set out to apply meaning to my suffering. It wasn't easy. If it were easy, everyone would do it, and I wouldn't feel compelled to write this story. Nothing worth anything comes easily in this world, and if it does, it usually goes away easily, too. Easy come, easy go.

I made a firm declaration. Not just a measly promise. I made the kind of declaration that was inscribed on my soul in letters of fire. I vowed to be courageous and disciplined. Let me explain something: it takes a lot of courage and discipline to endure the sharp pains of self-discovery required for spiritual growth. Many people, instead, opt to tolerate the dull pain of unconsciousness, and they resign themselves to it sometimes for a life-time.

Did you know the human spirit is much stronger than we give it credit for? I know that now. I know most people give up on themselves easily, but the human spirit is extremely powerful and incredibly impressive, especially if fueled properly.

Finding meaning in my misery helped me turn my heartbreak into something beautiful and worthwhile. Applying purpose to my suffering diminished the impact of those negative experiences and transformed them into something positive and beneficial. Loss and suffering are inevitable. But with meaning, with God, they are never wasted.

People say that no one can change the sound of an echo, but that's not true. The remaining echo of those memories no longer brought a grimace to my face, but rather a smile, the reverberation of them no longer haunting, but purposeful. You want to know how you change the sound of an echo? You change yourself. If you change yourself, then what you hear changes.

This new practice of mine, of finding purpose in all things, facilitated the building of emotional resilience. It helped me find my way back to my inner peace and stay there. It didn't happen overnight. The miracle I experienced, yes, that was instantaneous, but I still held the obligation of putting in the required effort in the period that followed. It remained my responsibility to nourish my own soul, to develop a partnership with God. The Bible says, "Draw near to God, and He will draw near to you" (James 4:8). For me, drawing near to God necessitated much discipline and practice. It still does to this day.

Faith, trust, hope, and love are not once-in-a-lifetime decisions. They have to be made, chosen, over and over again. It's a training of the mind. It's a conditioning of spiritual strength and stamina, of emotional endurance.

I reread the e-mails I exchanged with Wes. I revisited the keystrokes that deepened my love for him. I recalled how joyful I was when I focused on positivity, possibility, and love. I knew I could get back to that place of inner contentment again and travel to an even better place. I had gained so much ground, learned so many things, and they'd worked. They honestly worked. Maybe they didn't work the way I expected or as speedily as I wanted, but they unquestionably beat the alternative.

Truthfully, I was so used to taking an efficient elevator to my successes—quick, to the point, and with minimal effort—that this spiritual voyage seemed annoyingly slow and preposterously difficult. It didn't have an elevator that I could find, or if it did, it was out of order. I had to take the stairs, one insanely small step at a time, and that came as a big adjustment to me.

My generation and the generation following live in an era of instant gratification. Many of us have lost the aptitude to discipline ourselves presently to postpone pleasure in the short term in order to experience greater gratification in the long run. We also tend to throw away things that are broken rather than put the time and effort into fixing them. This mentality is partly why I had found myself in another depression following the breakup. I threw my broken spirituality out the window, and along with it went my inner peace.

I believe, now, more than ever before, that people *need* to lead spiritual lives, all of us. The people who don't, the unfortunate ones who become trapped on this material plane due to the limited scope of our senses, suffer more than those who access the infinite consciousness that is available to all people.

So many people believe reality is what we can confirm through the limited instruments of our senses, but reality is far beyond that. Anything that we describe through science alone, we describe through the narrow prism of our senses. Isn't it likely, then, that there are other forms of consciousness moving through the universe all around us that science cannot detect? Other vibrations, frequencies, and energies? I think it has to be there, in the non-quantum world, where the answers to everything lie.

Even if you are someone who believes only what you can qualify and quantify through the human senses and science, did you know that when you think positive, happy, loving, hopeful thoughts, there's a different chemistry that goes on inside your body than when you think depressing, negative, anguishing, despairing thoughts? Thoughts and expectations have been proven by science to be very powerful in the physical world.

Look, I know it's difficult for many of us to believe in things we cannot see, to easily access these mystical realms of spirituality. I've been there. Done that. I think we are, by nature, spiritual people, though. I believe all of us experience an internal yearning, a dissatisfaction of sorts, an itchy irritability that can only be satisfied through spirituality. If we don't have access to spirituality, I believe we suffer more as individuals. We suffer more as a society.

I came to recognize, through my own unique spiritual journey, that at some place within myself there is an infinite capacity for connection to unseen realms of power and peace. Everyone has that. You can't exactly see it, but you can feel it, primordially, if you are open to it.

I discovered this fact through the worst heartbreak and letdown I had ever known. What I thought would be the end of my biggest dreams and purest hopes turned out, instead, to be a glorious beginning of a life far grander than any I had ever previously imagined.

It's like Albert Camus said, "In the depth of winter, I finally learned that there was in me an invincible summer."

Chapter 24

Subject: Hey sweet girl
Friday, February 28, 2014, at 9:13 AM
To: Mila / From: Birdie

Dear Mila,

How's life sweet girl? It's been a few weeks since we've gotten together. The last time I saw you, you looked great!

I know you revealed that day how much you still sometimes miss Wesley, but I believe it's always better to make changes for oneself than to try to mend the holes torn by the decisions of others. In which case, I hope you're continuing to heal and move forward with your life. ☺

I just got back from the cancer retreat I was telling you about at Red Feather Lake. I love the Shambhala Mountain Center! It's so peaceful there. It's a six hundred acre mountain valley surrounded by dense forests, gentle meadows, and jagged rocky peaks. It truly is the perfect contemplative refuge.

As you know, I have long believed in the power of a deepened awareness to encourage personal wellbeing. I simply adore gathering there to experience Shambhala wisdom with accomplished practitioners and spiritual teachers. I've met some of my favorite people at this place.

Anyway, I was thinking about you while I was there. I'd like to share some of the things I learned.

There were two questions we were invited to ask ourselves in all circumstances going forward in our lives. 1) How would I act out of pure love? and 2) What would I do if I weren't afraid?

Why these two questions, you ask? Well, *A Course in Miracles* teaches that all human reactions derive from two of the most basic human emotions. Those emotions are either 1) love or 2) fear. Did you know that fear is actually the opposite of love, not hatred? Hatred, negativity, anger, jealousy, and the like all stem from fear. *A Course in Miracles* also says, "Heaven is a decision I must make." These two fundamental questions on love and fear, then, are intended to prompt us in making decisions that guide us to heaven—not just heaven in the afterlife but heaven on earth in this life, too.

Honestly, I was a little skeptical at first. I always believed that when the Bible said, "Heaven and earth shall be as one," it meant someday in the distant future, most likely after I was already dead! But now, I can see that heaven and earth shall be as one here and now, presently, and eternally. I kid you not, Mila, asking myself these two questions have produced subtle but remarkably powerful changes inside and around me. It's sort of like doing a somersault and landing in a brand-new reality, a place where you see things from a different perspective and experience things in a brand-new way.

Do you see what I'm trying to say, Mila? Heaven is not a place you arrive at one day. It's a lens you bring to the place you are right now, presently, and eternally.

I think there might be a moment in all of our lives, a tipping point when one particular bit of wisdom provides a new lens through which everything else suddenly looks clearer, better, and connected. It's why I love sharing my wisdom with you and others. Maybe something I pass along will help someone the way I've been helped. I hope so! ☺

I'd like to get coffee with you sometime in the near future. Would that work for you?

With love,
Birdie

P.S. There was a quote posted on one of the walls of the mountain center that I really loved. "The measure of trial you've endured directly relates to the measure of hope you offer the world. Press on." ~ Rebekah Lyons

---

Subject: Thank you!
Friday, February 28, 2014, at 3:15 PM
To: Birdie / From: Mila

Dear Birdie,

Thank you so much for the beautiful e-mail! I'd love to grab coffee with you this coming week. How about Monday?

It sounds like you had a very enjoyable experience at the cancer retreat this year! I love that you continue to share with me all of the wisdom you've been collecting over the years. I've learned so much from you, Birdie. Thank you for that. You're such an inspiration to me. The trials you've endured and risen above give me much hope. ☺

I'd also like to share some of the things I've learned recently. I've been doing a little research on how best to embrace total love, faith and fulfillment in my life. These are things I yearn for and things that give me peace and joy.

What I've learned (or rather what I've re-learned LOL) is that having an open mind and equally open spirit are key to embracing these things. Therefore, lately I've been striving for possession of what Zen Buddhism calls "Zen mind" or "beginner's mind." If you're not familiar, a "Zen mind" is like an empty rice bowl. It's open. It's free. Because once it's full, it can't receive more. This basically means that when you think you've figured it all out, you become unteachable.

You see, Birdie, we all think we know so much, or at least I did—for the longest time. There's this Taoist story that brought this concept to life for me, and I'd like to share it with you. It's a story of an old farmer who had worked his crops by horse for his whole adult life. One day, his horse ran away. His neighbors, upon hearing the news, came to visit and exclaimed sympathetically, "Your horse is gone. Such bad luck!"

The farmer replied, "Maybe. What do I know about good and bad luck?"

The next morning the horse returned, bringing with it several other wild horses. His neighbors, upon hearing the news, came to visit and exclaimed excitedly, "How wonderful! What good luck."

The farmer replied, "Maybe. What do I know about good and bad luck?"

The following day, the farmer's son tried to break one of the untamed horses and was thrown from the horse's back, breaking his leg. His neighbors, upon hearing the news, came to visit and exclaimed sympathetically, "Your son's leg is broken. Such bad luck!"

The farmer replied, "Maybe. What do I know about good and bad luck?"

Shortly thereafter, military officials came to the village to draft young men into the army for a gruesome and bigoted civil war. Seeing the son's leg was broken, they passed him by. His neighbors, upon hearing the news, came for a visit and exclaimed excitedly, "How wonderful! What good luck."

The farmer replied, "Maybe. What do I know about good and bad luck?"

In this story, Birdie, we see in one short series of events that we cannot know what lies ahead. None of us can. I, like the neighbors, thought I knew so much. Yet now I'm coming to understand that I'm better off to be like the old farmer and possess an "empty rice bowl" kind of perspective.

This concept goes hand-in-hand with understanding a healthy detachment from earthly outcomes and expectations. I'm beginning to see that depending on particular results for emotional nourishment is like depending on somebody else's hand to feed me. I now get that being too attached to personal attainments, expectations, and other people's opinions gives outside sources, those of which I have little to no control, the power to nourish me, and consequently, the power to starve me. On the other hand, discovering a healthy detachment from these things now permits me to fuel (to find value) from within.

I'm sure you can relate, Birdie, being a classic overachiever like myself, that it feels awfully unnatural to my personality to detach myself from results. As you know, I often found my self-worth in what I accomplished. I received immeasurable value from how I performed intellectually to how I looked physically. But when I inevitably failed to meet my own strenuous standards or failed to meet someone else's, the subsequent ego crash took a heavy toll on my heart.

Just quickly, allow me to clarify something. Ending dependency on outcomes does not mean I've abandoned goals or important relationships or that I've given away all of my belongings! LOL! It simply means I'm trying to open my heart and mind to all possibilities and to discover purpose and value in outcomes even if they deviate from my present hopes and desires. Like Rumi said, "Life is a balance of holding on and letting go." And this is true of everything. Life is one big, crazy balancing act, isn't it?!

My mom hung a quote on the fridge the other day. I think she left it there for me. It's about balance. It goes, "Healthiness and happiness are tucked somewhere between too little and too much."

Anyhow, I'll share more of what I've been learning with you on Monday, if that date works for you. I'm looking forward to seeing you and hearing more about the retreat!

With love,
Mila

After writing this e-mail to Birdie, it dawned on me that I'd actually started to scratch the surface of the concept of healthy detachment before I left to see Wes. I even shared a quote in one of my e-mails to him that said something along the same lines regarding romantic relationships.

But the breakup and my subsequent depression revealed to me the depth of my own dependency. The arrival of the unforeseen often has that effect: revealing the depths of your character. I learned the hard way that

I still had, and will likely always have, much work to do here.

Before I went out to see Wes, my rice bowl was pretty full. I thought I had figured things out. Remember? I held the secret. I cracked the code. So when things didn't turn out the way I figured they should, when I didn't achieve the results I desired, the fallout hit me hard. It jolted me so thoroughly my whole world came crashing down chaotically around me. It shook my faith so violently it threatened to bury it beneath the rubble, never to be exhumed. I thought I had turned my last sharp spiritual corner. So when I looked up to see a whole other unforeseen mountain yet to climb, the realization about killed me.

The good news is, the next time life decided to "deal me dirty," my effort to uphold a Zen mind helped me avoid another calamitous spiritual crash. It provided me the foundation I needed for emotional resilience.

In March, I finally decided to touch up the blonde highlights that I had let grow out way too far in my depression. I went to my usual hairdresser and had the usual product put on my roots, something I'd been doing for over a decade. So you might imagine my surprise when all of my blonde hair fell out.

My hairdresser said he had never seen anything quite like it before. It was as though I had a rare allergic reaction to the bleach and any hair that had touched it became stretchy and broke entirely off. He checked my hair halfway through the process and removed the bleach immediately once he noticed the strange reaction. It wasn't his fault. He certainly didn't over-process my hair or do anything wrong.

But it didn't matter. The damage was done. He felt awful, and urgently recommended that I see a doctor as soon as possible because he thought the reaction to the bleach was related to some health issue I hadn't yet discovered. He told me he learned about this kind of thing in school, though he had never seen it before, and said I must go see a doctor.

I vomited when I left the hair salon. I vomited right next to my car before I even opened the door. I thought about what the hairdresser said and started to worry that I really was sick. Maybe I had cancer. Maybe I had some kind of thyroid disease.

I knew the bumps on my face had something to do with my hair falling out. I felt it in my gut. I experienced an undeniable visceral feeling that the two were somehow related. Things weren't right with me, a lot of things. My general health was off somehow. It wasn't just my skin and now my hair. It was my lack of periods, my lack of an appetite, my excessive tiredness, and many other things that weren't normal. Yet I couldn't figure out what was causing all the problems. It especially frustrated me since I was eating healthier than ever before in my entire life and exercising regularly. Never before had I taken my health so seriously, so I wondered, exasperatedly, *what the FUCK is going on with me?*

I called my mom, bawling. She could hardly understand the words coming out of my mouth because I cried like a toddler having a tantrum. When I got home, my mom led me back to her bedroom, had me sit on her bed, and brushed through my hair like she did when I was a little girl. Clumps of blonde hair wadded up in the hairbrush to the point even she got sick.

She cried with me briefly, but then dried her tears promptly. She tried to make me feel better. She told me I was beautiful no matter what. She attempted to make light of the situation by joking with me and telling me how lucky I was to look so good in hats.

Behind her humor, I could tell she was really worried, though. I saw it written on her face. When I looked into her eyes, I could see tears and concern just behind the surface. She, too, thought I must be sick with some kind of serious, undiagnosed disease. She didn't say it, but she didn't have to.

That day, I rallied all of my inner grit and did my best to overcome my fears of being ugly and sick. I reminded myself that true beauty, eternal beauty, has nothing to do with what the eye physically sees. I told myself that true health, eternal health, has nothing to do with my physical being. I repeated banalities like "all of life's problems are opportunities to learn and grow" or "today's struggles are but seeds for tomorrow's blessings." But if I'm being completely frank, I was facing one of my steepest learning curves yet.

For the first time in my life, I felt absolutely revolting, so repulsive I didn't want anybody to see me ever again. I wanted to live under a paper bag. If I had been an ostrich in that moment, I would've stuck my head in the sand and refused to pull it out again.

Cruelly, I couldn't stop looking at myself in the mirror either. It was as though I needed to torment myself by constantly reminding myself how far I had fallen. Once a sassy, brassy beauty and the envy of other women, I was now ghastly and totally undesirable, at least on the outside. At least that's how it felt.

The thing is, I was so used to being eye candy and so new to being soul food that this lesson, in particular, profoundly tested and challenged me. I knew I was a little vain, but this lesson brought to light my deep-seated superficial ways. It took a long time, too, or so it seemed, before it went away. It took years for the bumps to recede and the hair to grow back. The bumps, even after they were gone, left small pockmark scars on my face and some pinkish discoloration of my once flawless skin.

One of the reasons this lesson presented a major challenge to me is because I had always been groomed from a very young age to believe that beauty was exceedingly important. Society continuously reinforced and confirmed this belief by treating me like I was special for being beautiful. It gave me the upper hand in most situations. It made life easier and more enjoyable. It gave me power. And I became greedy for it. Also, it was something tangible I could always fall back on, something I could easily (even if wrongly) point to as providing worth to my life.

Don't get me wrong. Beauty isn't bad. The desire for beauty isn't evil. God loves beauty, too. He appreciates and creates it. "He has made everything beautiful in its time" (Ecclesiastes 3:11). However, I believe something is off kilter if beauty starts superseding the more lasting, deeper human qualities like personality and character. I was obviously at a point in my life where the aesthetic scales were out of balance. Losing my hair forced this realization out of the dusky crooks of my mind into the light of consciousness.

In response to this realization, I began celebrating and focusing on deeper human qualities, in myself as well as others, every chance I got. As part of this progression in my perspective, I started redesigning my social media newsfeed, unfollowing certain people while giving those who promoted grander ideals higher priority by making them my favorites so they would show up in my newsfeed first.

Despite its pitfalls, social media has the potential to be amazingly positive and uplifting. It holds the power to inspire great changes in ourselves and our communities. It also maintains the ability to promulgate fear, negativity, hatred, and insecurity. It's all about how we decide to use it.

The hair misfortune, while initially very upsetting, turned out to be a good thing. It helped me fully grasp another area in my life demanding spiritual development. Like an empty rice bowl, I *tried* to stay open to the lessons it had to teach me. I emphasize the word *tried* because achieving Zen mind 100 percent of the time is impossible. Nobody is able to achieve this completely, but the striving for such is in itself part of the deliverance. It's the foundation for finding inner peace and maintaining a predominantly joyful existence.

Spiritual practice isn't perfect. Actually, it's quite messy. In the wake of my hair disaster, my knee-jerk reaction was to fall back on the belief that I'd find happiness again as soon as my hair grew back or maybe once my bumps were gone. I nearly went back to placing happiness on the peak of a mountain, as something singular, big, and impending on the horizon; something dependent on a particular outcome.

It required significant mental calisthenics, a continual finessing of my thoughts, to train my brain to see happiness not as something hidden around the next bend in the road, but as something present, ordinary, plentiful and attainable right where I was, Homer Simpson bald with toad skin or not.

A couple of days later, I ventured out into public for the first time. I went for a walk with my mom. I was feeling anxious about going to work the next day with my hair looking the way it did, so my mom suggested easing me into it by going for a walk around town. The thing about a small town is that people always see you and stop and talk to you when you're out and about. It was a good exercise for me, so I agreed to it.

While we were walking, my mom turned to me and said, "I gotta say, Mila, I'm proud of you for how you're handling all this."

I smiled weakly at her. "Thanks, Ma. I'm trying."

"I can see that you are, babe. You know what I really like about your approach to positivity?" I shrugged my shoulders and shook my head at her. "What I like is that you're so honest about it. It's not like you're trying to pour pink paint over your fears and negativities and pretend like they don't exist." She smiled and then linked arms with me.

"Yeah, well I guess I realize that denial and suppression of emotions can't be healthy either. What is clearly psychologically unsound is probably also spiritually unsound, don't you think?"

"Yes, definitely. I believe there's a time and place for tears and heartbreak in everyone's pilgrimage here on earth." She exhaled a long sigh before continuing. "The sorrows of this world are real, Mila, and crying is often the most befitting and heartfelt expression of our experiences. It is the authenticity of our love, after all, which often triggers our tears."

I nodded my head. "I like that, Ma. That's really beautiful."

We walked and I thought for a moment as I put my feelings together. "For me, a positive perspective has to be sustainable, I guess ... and never feeling sad is not realistic. Yet when it comes down to it, I keep coming back to the ultimate focus of my spirituality, which is never on the negativities of life but on God's unspeakable love for me and all He created and the certainty that life is good and it's eternal. For me, knowing this is the key to my gratitude and hope, which ultimately transcends all my grief."

My mom smiled at me then. "I sure do love our walks and talks, Mila. Havin' you home with us has been such a treat for me and your dad."

"I love them, too, Ma. You've been so good for my spirit. And finally building a relationship with Dad has been wonderful, too."

❧

Fast-forward a few years from that conversation, and I can tell you from my own experience that with dedication, everyone is capable of building emotional resilience by upholding a sustainable, positive perspective. It's a matter of practice. Practice is one of the most basic principles, isn't it? And behind every principle is a promise.

The more positive thoughts I conjured over time, the more automatic positive thoughts my subconscious mind generated. It's not rocket science. It's how I would go about training any kind of habit, good or bad. It got easier with time and persistence, too.

Another thing that got easier with time was smoking less pot. The healthier my body and spirit became, the less I enjoyed smoking. Eventually it stopped being as much fun for me.

I'm at a point now, years later, where I'm truly overwhelmed by the holiness of the everyday. It's kind of amusing because the everyday things themselves haven't changed. For example, birds and trees and flowers and squirrels are all the same, so are the sunrises, sunsets, and stars in the sky. But I never really saw them so clearly before. I guess somewhere along the line, I was struck with the simple truth that sometimes the most ordinary things can be made extraordinary simply by seeing or doing them with the right attitude.

How many people in this world don't wake up like I do? In a warm home, a comfortable bed, with a blanket and pillow, clean water, as much food as I want, and a family who loves me? Reminding myself to appreciate the "small" things when I wake helps me dress every morning with a pair of positive pants, a simple shirt of certainty, and various garments of gratitude. This creates a sense of abundance and more-than-enoughness, which is precisely the satisfaction and deep peace of my True Self that my Papa destined for me.

And afterward, I'm able to envision bits and pieces of sacredness that frame and embrace the humble routines and tasks of the commonplace. Nothing seems ordinary or trivial anymore. Nothing seems impossible.

Nowadays, I aim to move through the world with utter peace and patience, attempting to give attention and purpose to every task I perform, every person I engage, and every thought I possess—to live with true and pure intention. I strive to operate with an uncomplicated conviction, an unassuming trust, and an understanding that if I believe something, and it is born out of genuine love (i.e. aligned with my Source), then it is virtually guaranteed to pass, whether I witness it in this life or the next.

I keep a quote posted on my mirror by Christian Larson. It's sort of long, but I love it because it encourages me to live well. It goes like this:

"To be so strong that nothing can disturb your peace of mind. To talk health, happiness, and prosperity to every person you meet. To make all your friends feel that there is something in them. To look at the sunny side of everything and make your optimism come true. To think only the best, to work only for the best, and to expect only the best. To be just as enthusiastic about the success of others as you are about your own. To forget the mistakes of the past and press on to the greater achievements of the future. To wear a cheerful countenance at all times and give every living creature you meet a smile. To give so much time to the improvement of yourself that you have no time to criticize others. To be too large to worry, too noble for anger, too strong for fear, and too happy to permit the presence of trouble. To think well of yourself and to proclaim this fact to the world, not in loud words but great deeds. To live in faith that the whole world is on your side so long as you are true to the best that is in you."

Am I perfect in these practices? Hell no. Not even close. But that doesn't stop me. It doesn't discourage me, either!

Chapter 25

Spring arrived quickly, as if winter, like some un-welcome visitor, had brusquely shrugged its way into its frock and took off without a backward glance. Summer appeared even faster, shuttling the child of spring out the door like a busy, no-nonsense mother. And before I knew it, more than four seasons had passed since I last spoke to Wes.

I thought of him every single day, without exception. One might even be able to detect a stifled palpitation in my voice at the memory of an invisible presence in the room with me. You see, people who really matter in our lives stay with us indefinitely, subtly affecting our most regular and routine moments. Goodbyes, when it's all said and done, are merely for those who love purely with their eyes and their hands. For those who love with their soul, there is no total separation, only the partial separation that is physically observed in the present. That's the beautiful, and sometimes haunting, thing about love.

Sometimes I missed him so much it felt like my heart was beating outside my chest. Sometimes I felt like Tom in *The Glass Menagerie* who proclaimed, "Oh, Laura, Laura, I tried to leave you behind me, but I am more faithful than I intended to be!" But most times, I was okay ... No, wait, that's not actually true. I was *better* than okay. I was happy. Truly, deeply happy.

I hoped he was happy, too.

The year that had passed since I last spoke to him had been one of those that really "got my attention." Life seems to have a way of doing that from time to time. Over the year, I experienced new seasons of understanding and transformation I never thought possible. Relinquishing a thought system based largely on fear and negativity, by training my mind to focus on love and positivity, changed my whole life in ways many people would find impossible to believe.

Over the year, I finally found the missing pieces within for which I always longed. I found the woman inside me who knows what she's truly worth; whose said worth doesn't come from another human being or an accomplishment. A woman whose beauty beams from a radiant light within that sparkles and shines, touching others with warm embers of peace, compassion, and joy. A woman capable of admiring someone else's beauty without questioning her own. A woman who refuses to define others or herself by outward appearances.

I found the woman inside me who loves herself enough to renounce poisonous people, thoughts, and situations. A woman who seeks only the very best things and relationships in her life. A woman who desires to inspire and help others by using her God-given gifts, who isn't afraid to bust it each and every day to manifest her dreams and live the remarkable life she dared to imagine.

I found the woman inside me courageous enough to write and share this story.

Now, several years since embarking on this spiritual passage, my mind is hardly the touchstone of perfect loving perception. Try as I might, I won't pretend to constantly achieve a loving viewpoint in every situation all the time. One thing I'm very adamant about, though, is that when I do, life works better. And when I don't, things remain "blah" at best.

Each of us fights different fears, and each of us manifests our fears in different ways, but I truly believe all of us are healed by the same means: Love.

God is Love.

To address fear by any other means is a fleeting palliative, a fix but not a healing. We are all the same like that. There is a oneness to us all. Like Marianne Williamson illustrated in *A Return to Love*, we are like spokes of a bicycle wheel. We all connect to the same center. The problem is, most of the time we define ourselves according to our position on the rim, in which case we appear very different, sometimes completely opposite from one another. But if defined from our starting point, our Source, the center of the wheel, we share in the same identity.

One of the byproducts of spirituality, then, is the galvanizing of people. Bringing people together. Another byproduct is that the closer we identify with our Core, the deeper, more relatable and more attractive we naturally become.

Though I could never actually prove it, I believe it was this simple kind of attractiveness, this sort of special, mystic magnetism that eventually drew him back to me.

Chapter 26

Spring showers teased more green from the ground. The sky, now, was clear blue, with large cumulous clouds, slowly floating across the heavens like lazy bits of cotton. The air was gentle and sweet. Clusters of crocuses seemed to have bloomed overnight. The first of the potato shoots fingered their way out of the soft soil.

It was a sunshiny April morning. The ground was spongy with melted snow and rain, and it was one of those blessed, perfectly balmy days that perceptibly rejoiced the coming of summer.

I walked around the yard barefoot on a cashmere blanket of grass checking out all the new beautiful blooms. I dreamily soaked up the splendor of the day, periodically taking pictures of spring flowers on my iPhone.

And then it happened.

FRIDAY, APRIL 17

```
Wes: hey
```

My heart rolled over in my chest. I read the name again, wondering, at first, if my eyes had deceived me. I opened the text. It was limp, only a single word: "hey." But there it was. Short, plain, but deeply felt all the same. I had silently hoped to hear from him for over a year. And, now, at the sight of his name on my phone, a soft warmness blossomed throughout my body, and my fingers and toes felt pleasantly tingly.

I traced my fingers over the word as if it were a portrait rather than letters. I followed its graceful outline like I once followed the outline of his handsome features.

FRIDAY, APRIL 17

```
Mila: hi ☺
Wes:  long time no talk
Mila: yeah. how r u?
Wes:  not bad. u?
Mila: fantastic
Wes:  that's good ☺
Wes:  what's new
```

Mila: not much ... or maybe everything

Mila: depends on how u look at it

Wes: ?

Mila: lol still living with my parents. still
      working part-time at my job. but life
      is really really good now

Wes: glad ur doin well mila

Wes: my mom said u went out to lunch with
      her yesterday

Mila: yeah it was nice

Mila: ur mom has been a good friend to me

Wes: you've been a good friend to her

Mila: thanks

Wes: would u wanna grab a drink with me
      sometime

Mila: umm ...

Wes: c'mon. i'd like to talk to u

Mila: 'bout what?

Wes: just catch up

Mila: hmmm

Wes: lol it's just a drink

Mila: ha! i thought our first date was "just"
      dinner ... then look what happened

Wes: lol best night of ur life ☺

Mila: ur still full of yourself i see

Wes: maybe a little ☺

Wes: what if i promise u i won't have sex
      with u

Mila: oh geeh golly what a relief

```
Wes:   i'll ratchet down the charm factor for
       you. how 'bout that?
Mila:  lol u capable of that?
Wes:   it's tough but yeah
Mila:  haha ok weirdo
Wes:   so drinks then
Mila:  persistence huh?
Wes:   with u … it pays ☺
Wes:   pick u up at 6:30
Mila:  is that a request or a demand?
Wes:   that's an order ☺
```

Just before 6:30, I threw on a simple pair of heavily worn blue jeans with a clean gray T-shirt and a pair of flip-flops. I brushed through my now short hair. Not long after I had lost half of it, I cut it short, well above my shoulders, to start over fresh. I had been trimming it regularly to continue to slowly eliminate what was left of the damaged hair. I hadn't colored it since that fateful day, and finally, my head boasted nothing but thick, healthy hair with a completely natural glossy auburn tint. It rested just above my collarbones in an attractive A-frame fashion.

I briefly considered applying heavier makeup. My face still carried bumps. But I decided against it. I was actively trying to make peace with my skin every day, and part of my practice was to treat it with love and as if it were already as healthy as I wished it to be. Besides, my skin was healing. Albeit very slowly. Nevertheless, I sought to show my faith in the healing process and practice my patience. It was the least I could do for the gift of healing I had graciously received.

I had finally discovered a few months earlier that I was experiencing an allergic reaction to one of the multivitamins I had started taking religiously in my initial pursuit of healthiness. It was this allergic reaction that gradually accumulated in my system over the course of several months that eventually caused a whole pile of medical issues for me. I had found out that it caused a dramatic unbalancing of my hormones which triggered the bumps on my face, the loss of my hair a year earlier, the loss of my appetite and period, a most likely contributed to my depression.

I never suspected or would've imagined that a little vitamin could wreak so much havoc in my life. I investigated all sorts of possibilities, too, like food and product allergies, and requested doctors run all sorts of tests to see if it were some other underlying disease causing the problems, but we failed to identify this "harmless" pill in the process. I was, quite understandably, at my wit's end trying to figure out what was going on with me. Yet, I continued to hold trust in my healing, and eventually the answer came to me.

This may seem a little choreographed, but it's the truth. I discovered the link to the vitamin on my twenty-eighth birthday. I like to think of it as a birthday gift from my Papa.

I happened to "randomly" read one of the reviews online as I was about to purchase more of the vitamins from Amazon with a gift certificate I received from my sister, Reese. The review, hidden discreetly among countless positive reviews, said, "Caution! This pill caused a horrible allergic reaction resulting in tiny bumps on the skin of my face that won't seem to go away." A bright lightbulb flashed in my mind's eye. That's all I needed to read to know that the vitamin was the malefactor that was ravaging the health of my entire body, not just my skin.

I immediately stopped taking the pills and very steadily started noticing an improvement in my skin and overall health. *How ironic,* I thought, *that a pill I was taking to shortcut an improvement in my health did nothing short of battering it.*

Chapter 27

I saw his car pull up right at 6:30. He was always on time, never a minute late. My heart did a little happy dance as I grabbed my aviator sunglasses and a navy blue jacket and walked out the door to meet him before he entered the gate.

"Hi. Well don't you look as pretty as a peach parfait?" He said right away.

"Ha! Thank you." I half-laughed. "I thought you were gonna ratchet the charm down?" I raised an eyebrow at him, reminding him of his own promise.

"Well, I was gonna but ... I *really* like this natural look on you." He smiled genuinely at me. He pulled me in for a hug and squeezed, lifting me to my tippy toes. The scent of his Calvin Klein cologne washed over me, along with a thousand memories.

Our eyes met, and we both glanced away simultaneously as if suddenly realizing we had already given away too much of ourselves too quickly with one brief, intimate meeting of our eyes. He gently eased me down onto my feet again.

"You've gained weight," he said.

"Geeh, thanks," I replied, pretending to be insulted by the comment.

"It looks great on you, Mila. Looks like you put on 'bout fifteen pounds of muscle."

"Yeah almost. I've been lifting weights a few times a week." I flexed my tiny arm muscles at him. He laughed at my absurdity.

"Well, you look very ... " he broke off, hunting for the right word, " ... healthy," he finally finished, obviously choosing a more conservative word than he originally intended. I could tell by the shine in his eyes he wanted to finish that sentence differently.

"Thank you. I feel very ... healthy," I smiled at him. "Actually I feel really great, Wes." I beamed with a candid brightness I could not dim.

"Do you wanna grab a drink? Or I was thinkin' maybe we could just go for a walk?"

"A walk sounds nice. It's a perfect spring evening."

"I was hopin' you'd say that."

We started walking toward the park that was just four blocks from my parents' place. I had the strongest urge to grab his hand and fold it into my own. Instead, I tucked my hands in my jacket pockets.

"So I guess my mom probably told you she's gettin' brain surgery next week?"

"Yeah, she keeps me updated with her health. I'm sorry she's goin' through all that."

"Me too. She handles it with grace, though."

"I know. I really love that about her. She's been a real inspiration to me."

He nudged my arm with his elbow. "She enjoys your friendship. She *always* finds a way to bring you up in our conversations," he grinned at me as if *I* plotted this with her somehow.

"That's odd," I said. "We never talk about you."

"Never?" He eyed me doubtfully, and then looked almost offended.

"Well, almost never," I qualified. "She did tell me when you made it home safely over a year ago. You were traveling in a big snow storm. Remember? I think she was worried about you."

He interjected, "Oh yeah, that was bad. I almost had to give up and get a hotel room for the night. Some of the highways I planned to travel were closed."

I nodded and continued, "She also mentioned you started a laser engraving business a few months back.

Do you still operate the ballistic helmet business you were workin' on in Panama, too?"

"Yeah, the helmet business is doin' pretty well. I bought the laser engraver more as a hobby, but it somehow turned into a business." He grinned wryly at me.

"You're very entrepreneurial. I like that about you." I said politely. "I can imagine you now pursue profits with the same lethal enthusiasm with which you once pursued national enemies." I winked playfully in his direction.

He laughed. "Somethin' like that." He shook his head at my nerdy attempt at a joke. "I like bein' my own boss," he clarified. "I like workin' for myself for once."

"Yeah, I can't blame you that. I hope to be there myself someday."

"Have you started writing that book yet then?"

"Actually, I have." I smiled shyly at him, hoping he would not ask me what it was about. "I'm about four chapters in." I chuckled a little. "It's a lot more challenging and slower work than I thought."

"I bet. What's it about?"

I bit my lower lip as my innards squirmed like a worm about to be hooked. I stumbled my way through a response. "Um ... I'm not really sharin' details at the moment. It's a private work right now," I answered, while trying to neatly avoid further questions.

"Oh c'mon. Now I'm curious."

"I'll let you read it someday when it's ready," I said. I quickly added, "I promise," trying to pacify him.

"All right," he said, without disguising his disappointment. "Fair enough, I guess." As he said it, I thought I caught a flicker of something move across his face. *Was that sadness? Was he regretting our breakup?* It was honestly too hard for me to tell because whatever it was I saw in that instant, retreated as suddenly as it appeared.

We walked in silence for a bit when he surprised me by grabbing my arm and stopping me mid-step. "I'm really proud of you for startin' that book, Mila."

His sincerity was palpable. I don't know why, but it nearly moved me to tears. "Thank you," I murmured. My eyes drifted from his intense gaze down to the ground. Not knowing what else to say, I started walking again.

We walked and talked with ease. Completely engrossed, an hour passed in a flash, and before I knew it, the sun was setting. The air cooled rapidly, and despite our walking, I was getting cold.

"I bet you're gettin' chilly," he said, reading my mind.

"Yeah," I replied, wishing the sun would cooperate and shine on us forever so we could walk longer. I never tired of being with him.

"Well, let's head back." He grabbed my elbow and turned me toward the house.

As we approached his car I said, "It was nice catchin' up with you, Wes."

He looked at me and smiled deeply, revealing his shallow dimple. "Wanna do it again sometime?"

I couldn't help it, a cheeky grin took over my whole face. "Sure," I said without a moment's delay.

He grabbed me by the waist and planted a soft kiss on my cheek. He pulled back and looked at me with a peculiar look on his face. "You're different somehow, Mila," he said as a ridiculously charming crooked smile started at the corner of his mouth.

"Different?" I asked.

"Yeah, different. I don't know. Calmer or something." He laughed a little. "I don't know how to put it, just Zen."

I rejoined, "Yeah. Zen."

"I like it," he said. "Whatever it is, I really like it."

"Thank you. Me too."

He smiled at me again, and I thought I could see an entire range of emotions pass across his gleaming eyes. Happiness, remorse, confusion, compassion, and even love. Yes, love. Could I really see all that? Or was I projecting?

He kissed me one more time on the cheek. "I'll text you," he said as he opened the car door.

"Okay." I replied, feeling a spark of heat on my cheek where his lips left a small wet spot.

My legs wobbled as they transported me back to the house. I went in. I went straight to my bedroom in the basement, closed the door and leaned up against it. Tears filled my eyes. Love swelled in my heart. Gratitude overwhelmed my body as I slowly sank to the floor. "Thank you, Papa" was all I could say, and I repeated it several times.

SATURDAY, APRIL 18

```
Wes:   hey
Mila:  hi ☺
Wes:   i really enjoyed catchin' up with you
       yesterday
Mila:  me too
Wes:   dinner next friday?
Mila:  sure ☺
Wes:   can't wait ☺
```

That Friday he took me to a romantic Italian eatery called Pinocchio's with red brick walls and red-and-white-checked picnic table linens. We filled our conversation with his mother's health. I asked about her surgery, and he filled me in with all the details of her initial recovery.

"Can I ask you somethin'?" I inquired after the waitress had taken our order.

"Shoot," he said breezily.

"Why are you doin' this?"

"Doin' what?" He looked more concerned than confused.

"Taking me out."

He sat there and studied me for a long moment before answering. "Because I miss you, Mila."

The nudity of his words caught me by surprise as if he were sitting there in the restaurant completely stripped of his clothes. Another long pause followed as I processed his response. I swirled the ice in my glass with my straw, too timorous to look him in the eyes. "What happened in Louisiana, Wes?" I lifted my lashes to meet his gaze.

He shook his head. "I don't know, Mila. I honestly don't. I wish I could give you an answer. Things weren't right. That's all I know." I wondered if I imagined the pang of remorse in his voice.

"Oh," was all I could say in return.

"I know I hurt you."

"Yeah." My heart temporarily tightened at the memory of the terrible pain. Then, I sat up in my seat a little. "It's okay, though. It was good for me." I smiled at him.

He laughed, then—a light, friendly laugh. "I like that about you."

"Like what?"

"How you take somethin' bad and turn it into somethin' good."

"Thanks. It's not always easy."

"I know. That's why it's so attractive."

"You think I'm attractive?" I jokingly twirled my hair between my fingers and gave him a silly smile before I said, "Do I make you randy, baby?" in my best Austin Powers voice.

He laughed so hard he almost choked on the drink he was sipping. And I supposed nothing made me happier than to watch his rigid, muscular frame collapse into unruly happiness. I loved his laugh.

Then he became serious all at once and seized my hand from across the table. "Listen, Mila. There's something I've been wantin' to say to you." The words seemed to exit him with considerable effort, as though he were tugging them out from a secret place where he had been hiding them. "You'll have to excuse me if this sounds a little rehearsed. I've been thinkin' about it for a while now."

He cleared his throat before he began. "Explaining my feelings has been something of a weakness of mine, but also a protection. Thick skin and outward emotionlessness have served me well in many ways from a child up until recently in my world. I'm slowly figurin' out, though, that in this other world of family, friends, and ... especially you, that loving emotion is not something to be buried, but placed upon all of those around me.

"You see, meeting you poked holes in my hard exterior. I'd never fallen in love before and somehow you seeped into the cracks, bringin' with you a light I didn't know existed. And now," he interrupted himself by laughing. He ran his fingers through his hair before saying, "And now you just won't leave my life."

My heart kicked madly inside my ribcage like it was practicing some form of martial arts. I thought it might try to escape my chest it thumped so wildly. *Did he just say he loved me?* I wasn't sure if he was trying to tell me he still loved me or if he was simply explaining how he used to love me and how falling in love for the first time changed him somehow.

"That's sweet 'n' all, Wes but ... I did leave your life ... remember? You asked me to."

He faltered for a split second before replying, "You never *really* left, though. I still thought about you every damn day." His eyes dropped to the glass in his hand. "I've never wanted to admit it, but now I think I made a mistake in Louisiana." He looked at me again, searching my eyes for something, maybe forgiveness. "Things weren't right between us, Mila. You know that as well as I do. But there was more goin' on than just that."

"Like what? What else was going on? I never understood it."

"That makes two of us." He laughed lightly again. "I don't know for sure what was goin' on." He took another sip of his whiskey as if to take a moment to ponder it or perhaps to loosen his nerves. "I'll try my best to explain what I think might've happened because I know it's important for you to understand. So here's the thing, I don't know if I ever felt like our relationship was real until I came home and faced the fact that we would be livin' in the same state and actually carryin' on a normal relationship. Up until that point, our relationship was what it was. You know? It never infringed on my life because it rarely went beyond my computer or iPhone. Don't take that wrong." He squeezed my hand. "You were real to me. My love for you was real. But a real relationship is a real commitment, and I was adjusting to what that meant in a 'normal' life. I think the reality of it hit me when you came to visit and it scared me, or at least made me think twice about it.

"And that's the other thing. I was adjusting to a 'normal' life. My life had been anything but normal since I graduated high school." He stopped for second as if to accentuate the next bit. "I *loved* my job, Mila. Yes, it was my choice to leave active duty, but it was a difficult one. I felt like I needed to come home to spend some time with my mom. And meeting you played a part in that decision as well. Also, there's some stuff with the military that just gets old after a while, like all the red tape. But all in all, Mila, I loved my job. I love the guys I worked with. There is a bond that is formed in that kind of brotherhood that can never be replicated in the civilian world. I'm not sure you'll ever be able to understand that. I think a part of me felt a little guilty for leavin' behind my team. I didn't like doing that.

"I was obviously unsettled in my decision to leave, and I can't help but wonder if you weren't a little too real of an example of just how much my life was about to change. Maybe that's why I pushed you away."

He inhaled deeply and smiled as he exhaled away emotions he'd apparently been holding onto for some unknown amount of time. I enfolded his hand deeper into my own as if to suggest my acceptance of his explanation. "Yeah, I can see that. That makes sense. I wish you would've talked to me about it instead of pushing me away, though."

He nodded his head. "Pushing you away was a mistake." He shifted in his seat and leaned across the table slightly so that his face was closer to mine. "I want you back, Mila. But you have to know, I'm gonna make mistakes. I'm not perfect."

I felt full of static electricity, like someone had rubbed a balloon all over the hairs on my body and head. *Is this really happening?* Hearing all the words that had been bouncing off the walls of my brain for more than a year felt surreal. I wanted to inconspicuously pinch myself to make sure I wasn't dreaming. Instead, I looked at him and said with complete honesty, "I don't want perfect, Wes. I just want you."

His eyes lit up the room and a smile overhauled his entire face, and for once, I didn't fight not to lose myself within the pools of his deep brown eyes. For once, I permitted myself to be swept away by him with no fear or hesitancy or anything else to prevent me from just free falling in love.

Then the waitress brought our plates, and we released each other's hands so she could place them in front of us. We ate slowly, enjoying the happy energy indubitably doing the tango through both our systems.

We finished our meal and he held my hand as we walked back to the car. He opened my door for me and before I climbed in, he pulled me toward him for a kiss. When he drew back, he stared down at me and the love burning in his eyes scorched and charred away everything bad from our past. All the pain. All the confusion. All the anger. It was just us again. Just our love, deep and powerful, unmixed with any other emotion.

"I love you," he said. He repeated himself, with more emphasis the second time. "Mila, I still love you."

The sound of those words from his lips, floating dreamily like mid-summer cottonwood fluff softly to my ears, left my face tickling and my eyes shimmering.

"I love you, too," I whispered. "I never stopped."

He pulled me close and ran his fingers along the delicate white underbelly of my forearm, gentle as the whisper of a spider's legs gliding along silk. We touched each other softly, as if for the first time. His hand slid carefully across the small of my back. My fingers, slowly, deliberately, traced the perfect lines of his face. We were extra gentle with each other now, as if we finally discerned our own human fragility; as if we understood, now, what incredibly precious gift we might damage if we didn't handle each other with extra care.

With the delicateness of someone holding something irreplaceable, like you might imagine a first-time parent handling his newborn child, he took my body into his own. Under his breath, as if releasing a secret he had held on to for a long time, he quietly said, "I'm sorry, Mila. I'm so sorry for hurting you. For givin' up on us."

I looked up at him, solemn at first. A part of me was tempted to ask him to promise me he wouldn't do that again, that he wouldn't leave me like that again. I didn't, though, because the real world isn't like that. It's not simplistic like the ideas from a fairy-tale.

Life is an ambiguous thing. You never know what's around the next corner or how your next struggle might lead you to your next triumph. In an empty-rice-bowl kind of way, I let the thought go.

Then, a big, curly grin spread across my face so far my lips could stretch no further. "Meh," I shrugged my shoulders. "It'll be fine."

Epilogue

When I first started writing this book, I hadn't a clue how I'd finish it. I assumed it would end with me being single and happy. That's where I was in my life, after all. I expected it would conclude with me finding my innermost harmony by healing my most important relationship, my relationship with my Papa, and in turn, myself. And that, alone, would have been a great ending.

I had come to terms with the fact that my relationship with Wes was possibly just one of many necessary steps in my journey of enlightenment. I trusted God's plan for my life. I trusted His declaration that He had "plans to prosper [me] and not harm [me], plans to give [me] hope and a future" (Jeremiah 29:11).

My heart stayed open to all possibilities, like an empty rice bowl, open to receive the loving destiny I knew my Papa designed for me, however that looked. I obviously still loved Wes, and a wiser part of me wasn't ready to write him off. Not yet. So I left the ending unknown, unplanned, unwritten. My outline dawdled in a partial status for years after I began writing.

I'm glad for it, too, because my Papa wrote an ending to this book bigger and better than I planned for myself. He tends to do that, you know, make better plans, if you're open to them.

Never had I ever experienced an easier, more joyful, and deeply intimate love in my life than with Wes. We both entered the relationship the second time spiritually whole, in a sense.

For once, I was genuinely not looking for a man to complete me. For once, I kept a tight rein on my ego, which had proven skilled in previous relationships in its power-hungry determination to try to control my partner for my own benefit. For once, I did not welcome the fear and insecurities that yield all the craziness. I didn't worry, walking around with an umbrella, anticipating the rain. For once, I effusively embodied the spirit God gave me. "For God gave us a spirit, not of fear, but of power and love and self-control" (2 Timothy 1:7).

The second go-around, our love was unstoppable. Not because we didn't have failures and difficulties, that much is for sure. We had our differences, but our relationship strengthened every day. We learned how to withstand the squalls and adjust our sails accordingly, how to read the winds preemptively and navigate the unpredictable seas of life together. Like the sails, we became adaptable and, consequently, unbreakable in our love for one another.

Right off the bat, we shared an amazing romance, but over time we nurtured an even more powerful and essential friendship. In the past, I glorified romantic love. And in so doing, I poisoned many of my relationships by overvaluing their romantic content.

I once read a beautiful illustration of the vital relationship between friendship and romance. The relationship was illustrated with the image of a long-stemmed rose. The stem represented the friendship, the blossom the romance. Obviously, the more exciting, attractive part of the flower is the beautiful, colorful blossom. Because most of us are sensation-oriented, our focus automatically goes to the petals. Yet all the nourishment to the petals travels through the stem. And so it is, too, with a healthy relationship. There will come seasons when the petals fall off, but if the stem remains viable, the flower will bloom again.

Approximately one year after we started dating again, Wes asked me to accompany him on a river cruise in Eastern Europe with his family. Birdie's health was beginning to decline after her second brain surgery, and this vacation was something she wished to do with her whole family. The cruise included Romania, Bulgaria, Serbia, Croatia, and Hungary.

At sunset, on the ship's upper deck, as we drifted through the most majestic part of the Danube River locally called the Cataracts, with Serbia on my left and Romania on my right, Wes wrapped his arms around me from behind and placed a simple gold ring in front of my eyes. It was his great grandmother's wedding ring. I recognized it as one of the rings Birdie often wore and loved.

"Marry me," he softly murmured in my ear. To me, it sounded more like a harmonic serenade than a proposal.

My heart rolled over and trembled. I turned to face him. Without waiting for an answer, he slipped the ring on my finger and sealed it with a warm kiss.

Honestly, I knew the proposal was coming. I just didn't know exactly when or how. We talked about marriage often, and we both knew we wanted to spend our lives together. I had felt the perfectly sized jewelry box in his pocket a few days earlier and teased him about it. We were so close, it was practically impossible for us to keep secrets from one another.

Yet somehow, the moment still managed to take my breath away. "Yes." I finally exhaled the word we both knew was making its way out of me, after what seemed like forever in catching my breath.

Two short months later, we eloped. Several months following that, we held a small, intimate wedding reception at WeatherBee Ranch with our immediate family only. It was picture perfect, and we were truly blessed Birdie was able to attend because God called her home not long after.

We honeymooned in the Caribbean on a sailboat, earning our American Sailing Association certifications, which brought us one step closer to fulfilling our dream of captaining and living part-time on our own catamaran someday. A group of dolphins played by our boat while we traveled between islands, and I felt Birdie's undeniable presence as I watched them happily race and perform acrobatics near the bow of the boat.

Right after we returned from our honeymoon, with our loved ones, we spread Birdie's ashes in the Rocky Mountains on the family vacation property where she created endless loving memories, a beloved and cherished place rich with sentimentality.

About a year later, Wes and I built our first home, a beautiful log cabin on the property where Birdie's ashes blessed the soil. To me, it's the most magical place on earth. I like to think we somehow struck some sort of priceless bargain with the Birdie spirit on the other side of the veil to procure such magical beauty.

Today, I cannot imagine a more fortunate existence.

Oh, and yes, in case you were curious, I did befriend a fox! Well, sort of. He comes near the cabin often. He's a fetching young thing with amber eyes and a lovely red coat. I like to call him Fletcher, mostly because it alliterates well with fox ... and frisky and frolicsome and all the other festive adjectives I associate with him.

And now to make friends with a sea otter ... ☺

Acknowledgements

I would like to express my gratitude to the many people who saw me through this book. It was a long time coming, years in the making, and I am deeply appreciative to those who provided support, offered critical feedback, and assisted in the editing, proofreading, and design.

First, I would like to convey my utmost appreciation to my husband, Kit, who encouraged me to share my words with the world and who inspired me to write this book. Also, I owe him a big "thank you" for allowing me to share our most private interactions and communications in the intimate retelling of our story.

I would also like to thank my family and friends, especially my mom, my sisters, and my good friend, Jillian. Thanks to my mom, Connie, for being my very best friend and for helping me through some of my darkest hours, my sisters, Jenny and Ashleigh, for their remarkable contributions to the beautiful design of my book, and my good friend, Jillian, who first edited my manuscript and provided incredibly thoughtful and valuable feedback and encouragement.

I would like to communicate my sincere gratitude to my content and copyeditor, Monica, for her meticulous review of my work, her brilliant suggestions, and her warm and welcoming personality.

I would like to send thanks to Heaven to my mother-in-law, Betsy, who played a pivotal role in my journey of learning and healing and who continues to watch over us and deliver miracles from the other side of the rainbow bridge.

Above all else, I would like to give thanks to my Papa for blessing me with the courage and talent to tell this story and for granting me the greatest gift of inner peace.

About the Author

If you really want to know about Rebecca Rose, all you have to do is crack open her book, *It'll Be Fine*. Seriously. It's like dipping deep into her diary.

But here's something for you to chew on in the meantime ...

Rebecca first discovered her talent for writing in the third grade when she won a literary prize for a story about her cat, Dr. Benny Foo-Foo. Since then, her pets' names haven't improved much, but she likes to think her talent for writing has.

She now lives with her handsome husband and dog (whom they lovingly refer to as a vicious velociraptor) in the colorful state of Colorado.

If you enjoyed this book,

please leave a review on

Amazon and tell others!

Made in the USA
Middletown, DE
04 January 2017